A VERY HUMAN FUTURE

Enriching Humanity in a Digitized World

www.fastfuture.com

A VERY HUMAN FUTURE

First published in United Kingdom and United States of America by

Fast Future Publishing in 2018

http://www.fastfuture.com

For Information contact info@fastfuture.com

Paperback ISBN 978-1-9999311-3-1

eBook ISBN 978-1-9999311-2-4

Cover Designed by PixelStudio

Interior design and typesetting by Consilience Media

Print production by Print Trail

A VERY HUMAN FUTURE

Enriching Humanity in a Digitized World

Authors

Rohit Talwar
Steve Wells
Alexandra Whittington
Helena Calle

Edited by

Rohit Talwar

www.fastfuture.com

ABOUT FAST FUTURE

Fast Future is a professional foresight and publishing firm specializing in delivering keynote speeches, executive education, research, and consulting on the emerging future and the impacts of change for global clients.

We publish books from leading future thinkers around the world, exploring how developments such as AI, robotics, exponential technologies, and disruptive thinking could impact individuals, societies, businesses, and governments and create the trillion-dollar sectors of the future.

Fast Future has a particular focus on ensuring these advances are harnessed to unleash individual potential and enable a very human future.

www.fastfuture.com
Twitter @fastfuture @futrbiz
www.facebook.com/FutrBiz
www.linkedin.com/company/fast-future-publishing

THE AUTHORS

Rohit Talwar is a global futurist, award-winning keynote speaker, author, and the CEO of Fast Future. His prime expertise lies in helping clients understand and shape the emerging future. He has a particular interest in how we can create a very human future by putting people at the center of the agenda. Rohit is the co-author of Designing Your Future, lead editor and a contributing author for *The Future of Business* and *Beyond Genuine Stupidity—Ensuring AI Serves Humanity*, *The Future Reinvented—Reimagining Life, Society, and Business*, editor of *Technology vs. Humanity*, and co-editor and contributor for two forthcoming books: *Unleashing Human Potential—The Future of AI in Business* and *50:50—Scenarios for the Next 50 Years*.

rohit@fastfuture.com
Twitter @fastfuture
www.facebook.com/RohitKTalwar
www.linkedin.com/in/talwar

Steve Wells is a global futurist, keynote speaker, and the COO of Fast Future. He has a particular interest in helping clients anticipate and respond to the disruptive bursts of technological possibility that are shaping the emerging future. Steve is a contributor to *Beyond Genuine Stupidity—Ensuring AI Serves Humanity*, *The Future Reinvented—Reimagining Life, Society, and Business*, and a co-editor of *The Future of Business*, *Technology vs. Humanity*, and forthcoming books on *Unleashing Human Potential—The Future of AI in Business* and *50:50—Scenarios for the Next 50 Years.*

steve@fastfuture.com
Twitter @informingchoice
www.facebook.com/stevewells.futurist
www.linkedin.com/in/wellssteve

Alexandra Whittington is a futurist, writer, foresight director of Fast Future, and faculty member on the Futures program at the University of Houston. She has a particular expertise in future visioning and scenario planning. Alexandra is a contributor to *The Future of Business*, *Beyond Genuine Stupidity—Ensuring AI Serves Humanity*, and *The Future Reinvented—Reimagining Life, Society, and Business*, and a co-editor for forthcoming books *Unleashing Human Potential—The Future of AI in Business* and *50:50—Scenarios for the Next 50 Years.*

alex@fastfuture.com
Twitter @alexandra4casts
www.linkedin.com/in/alexandra-whittington-86794876

Helena Calle is a researcher at Fast Future. She is a recent graduate from the MSc. program in Educational Neuroscience at Birkbeck, University of London, and has eight years of international experience as a teacher, teacher trainer, pedagogic coordinator, and education consultant. Helena coordinates Fast Futures' growing research on the future of learning and is the curator and co-editor of a forthcoming book on The Many Futures of Education and Learning.

helena@fastfuture.com
Twitter @Helena_Calle
www.linkedin.com/in/helena-calle-5a6049135

Contents

Introduction
—A Very Human Future

Rohit Talwar

*How can we ensure that technological progress
doesn't leave humanity behind?*

A Mobilization Call

An almost daily flow of survey data and research reports are confirming that, across society, in the face of seemingly relentless and potentially incomprehensible technological advances, a growing number of people are becoming increasingly worried about their future and that of humanity. There are legitimate concerns ranging from the implications for individual and society through to the prospects for the global economy, the environment, and the distribution of wealth. While for some, these might seem insurmountable from where we are today, as optimistic futurists and strong believers in humanity's capacity to innovate and adapt, we believe there are many possible, if potentially challenging, paths to the future through which we can tackle those issues. These are the ideas and possibilities we introduce in *A Very Human Future—Enriching Humanity in a Digitized World*.

This book is an exploration and call to pursue actions that we can initiate today to preserve and enhance what it means to be human. We have no desire to slow the path of innovation or hold back the pursuit of goals that once seemed like the realms of science fiction.

1

Hence, across the pages of this book, we argue that we must ensure that the power of exponential and increasingly intertwined developments in science and technology is harnessed for the betterment of all who inhabit the planet. To achieve such ambitions, we cannot allow ourselves to be constrained by a scarcity mindset, outdated thinking, and self-restricting thoughts and beliefs about our capacity to change.

Artificial Intelligence and the Exponentials

The underlying force driving much of the concern about humanity's prospects is the relentless pace of development of a range of exponentially advancing technologies, key among them being artificial intelligence (AI). After many false dawns AI is now at a stage in its development where it is transforming industries and holding out the potential for even more radical future developments. It is also a critical enabler to the advancement of a range of converging fields including machine learning, robotics, autonomous vehicles and drones, big data, cloud computing, the Internet of Things (IoT), 5G networks, hyperconnectivity, quantum computing, 3D/4D printing, smart materials, synthetic biology, human augmentation, and space exploration.

The underlying purpose and goal of AI is to create intelligent software and hardware that can replicate or surpass critical mental faculties in order to work and react like humans. Hence, key applications include voice recognition, language translation, speech generation, image and video interpretation, learning, reasoning, inference, negotiation, collaboration, strategizing, planning, decision-making, and intuition. There are several underlying disciplines that are often included under the broad definition of AI, including big data, data mining, rules-based (expert) systems, neural networks, fuzzy logic, machine learning (ML), deep learning (DL), generative adversarial networks, cognitive computing, natural language processing (NLP), robotics, and the recognition of speech, images, and video.

What sets AI aside from all other innovations in history is its ability to learn and evolve autonomously. So, while previous machines and software have followed instructions, AI can make its own decisions, execute a growing range of tasks, and, increasingly, update its own knowledge base and code. The claims of near limitless potential are driving both the pursuit of opportunity and the perception that society is ill-informed and underprepared for the breadth of impacts AI and its disruptive cousins might have in the next two decades. It is these opportunities and impacts that we seek to explore in this book.

Societal Grand Challenges

Across the seven sections of this book, we set out to explore the likely development path and possibilities of these exponential technologies and how society can ensure they stay in service of humanity. Clearly, the notion of securing *A Very Human Future* requires us to address a broad range of issues, concerns, and opportunities that range from individual priorities to whole of society challenges. At the base level is the debate over technology's impact on job loss versus job creation and how we can pre-empt the worst-case scenarios. This in turn drives questions over how to raise levels of digital literacy and soft skills, and upgrade education provision throughout society. The potential for job loss to precede job creation forces us to consider issues of how we will feed our families, the role of mechanisms such as guaranteed basic incomes, and the potential growth in an underclass completely detached from the rest of humanity.

From an economic standpoint, technological disruption raises questions over how to fund the transition across the messy middle to new sustainable models for the economy. Defining and establishing those models will require creativity and experimentation with their design and new ideas on how to generate new jobs and sectors. The prospect of handing ever-greater power to the machine also drives concerns over increased weaponization of technology and the impact of growing digital dependency on the culture and the fabric of society. For individuals in this scenario there is concern over a potential loss of agency and self-determination, the risk of individuals becoming servants of the machine, and of getting lost in the matrix. Ultimately, the debate may come down to the simple issues of who owns the future and what say the ordinary citizen will have in its creation. It is these issues, the questions they raise, and some of the possible routes to solutions that we seek to explore in *A Very Human Future—Enriching Humanity in a Digitized World.*

The book is designed such that each short chapter can be read as a standalone provocation to explore an issue or development and its potential implications for society. Each chapter concludes with three questions about how the subject matter might impact you, your organization, or wider society. We hope you enjoy the wide array of topics covered and welcome your feedback on how you see the path unfolding to *A Very Human Future.*

A Very Human Future–Enriching Humanity in a Digitized World

To help explore the many issues and opportunities society must address, the seven sections of the book cover the following underlying topics:

PART 1: Technological Bursts of Possibility and Disruption

Future Snapshots–A 25-Year Outlook–Sets the scene for the book by presenting snapshot scenarios of how critical and complex social, geo-political, economic, and technological factors might play out and interact over the next 25 years.

Harnessing Technological Bursts of Possibility–Highlights some of the technologies that are disrupting our world, the new industries and job opportunities they will enable, and the vital roles of foresight and people-centric thinking in ensuring a viable future of our firms and our people.

The Future Evolution of Artificial Intelligence–Demystifies the fundamentals of AI, provides insights into seven possible stages through which it might develop, and highlights the types of applications we might see in the next 15-20 years.

Disrupting the Future for the Better–20 Robotics and Connected Devices that Could Impact Our Future Lives–Presents examples of how robotics and connected devices in particular could change a range of life experiences—hopefully for the better.

PART 2: Society and Social Policy

Is Automation Destined to Rewrite all Our Futures? Three Futurist Perspectives–Outlines three alternative futurist perspectives on how advances in technology could impact notions of employment, jobs, and income.

Will Real-Life Blade Runners be Tax Collectors?–Discusses the extent to which robots might penetrate society and the resulting social policy challenges.

Key Uncertainties About the Future of Women–Presents key challenges and visions of how business and society can adjust to ensure a more positive future for women and address critical agenda issues.

Fembots vs. HAL–Gender, Bias, and the People of AI–Reviews the growing trend toward anthropomorphizing AI technology and asks what this might tell us about the future of gendered technology.

Disrespectful Tech–Ten Ways Artificial Intelligence Could Transform Your Finances and Your Life–An overview of ten ways in which AI might impact and enhance our experience of personal banking.

The Big Reboot, Part 1–Rethinking Education and Employment in an Automated Era–Practical proposals for how we can reskill society and create new job opportunities in the face of widespread and accelerating automation.

The Big Reboot, Part 2–The Economic Impacts of Societal Transitions–Sets out a range of options to address a rise in the number of "technologically unemployed" and fund the costs of navigating a turbulent economic transition period.

PART 3: Human-Centered Cities

The Path to Smart–Mapping the Rise of Tomorrow's Smart Cities– Lays out a timeline of how the smart city story might evolve from hype to action in the coming decade.

*The Intelligence Premium–Smart Models for Smarter Living in the Smartest Cities–*Discusses how exponential technologies could help us design and deliver an enhanced city living experience.

*The Future of Multimodal Transport in a Self-Driving World–*Examines scenarios for the evolution of multimodal transportation in a self-driving future and the implications for citizens and society.

*Housing 2030–A Better Way of Living?–*Looks at how an array of technologies such the IoT and big data could shape our homes and living experiences.

*City Farming–Beyond Vertical Solutions–*Asks how indoor farming solutions could deliver the food requirements of a growing and more affluent urban population.

PART 4: People, Jobs, Capability

*Choosing a Human Path to the Future–*Outlines ideas on the future roles for people in an automated world and the implications for human-to-human relations.

*What Will Our Children Do? 20 Jobs of the Future–*Introduces examples of the kinds of jobs those currently in school or higher education might be doing when they enter the world of work.

*Five Business Shifts that Will Put Learning at the Heart of the Agenda–*Summarizes five underlying forces at play that are placing learning and development (L&D) at the heart of organizational survival and growth strategies.

Learning into a Faster Future–Suggests how we can prepare the learning and development function for the immense opportunities that lie ahead.

Five Possible Uses of Big Data in Future Learning Solutions–Highlights powerful emerging and potential applications of big data to improve the human learning process.

Enhancing Learning Outcomes with Virtual Reality–Describes current and potential high-impact applications of virtual reality to enhance the learning experience in education and the workplace.

PART 5: Business, Work, and the Workplace

Implementing AI in the Workplace–The Leadership Development Challenge–Provides key insights on how we can raise the capabilities of business leaders to operate effectively in an AI-enabled work environment.

Blockchain and the New World of Work–Reviews how blockchain technology could impact jobs by reshaping a range of work tasks and the management of workspaces.

AI and SMEs:–How Small to Medium Enterprises Can Take Advantage of the Technology–Presents examples of the applications and strategies SMEs can adopt to take advantage of AI's potential and help secure their future.

Humans and Work in the Digital Era–The Next 20 Years–Puts the spotlight on the possibilities of what organizations in our digital future might look like and how we will work.

Workplace 2040–Explores how our physical workplaces and working environments might evolve over the next 20 years.

PART 6: Industry Transformation and Disruption

The Future of Energy–Reinvented–Sets out a range of alternative, surprising, and unexpected future scenarios of how our energy futures might play out.

20 Ways Business Meetings and Events Might Change in the Next Five Years–Outlines example developments that could potentially become major industry trends as the sector evolves to meet the needs of an increasingly digitized delegate community.

Artificial Intelligence and the IT Professional–Discusses how the nature of opportunities and roles for the IT profession might be reshaped by intelligent machines.

AI in Financial Services–Applications and Challenges–Asks what the potential implications might be of artificial intelligence taking greater control of financial services.

A Perfect Storm? Factors Driving the Risks of Financial Armageddon–Outlines potentially disruptive forces that could drive the next global financial crisis.

PART 7:
Conclusion–Mapping a Very Human Future–Presents a mobilization call to individuals, businesses, civil society, and governments, highlighting critical priorities to ensure we start acting today to ensure a very human future.

PART 1:
Technological Bursts of Possibility and Disruption

Future Snapshots —A 25-Year Outlook

Rohit Talwar, Steve Wells, Karolina Dolatowska, Helena Calle, Alexandra Whittington, April Koury, Wendy Schultz, Guy Yeomans, Peter Stevens, and Kaat Exterbille

How might key aspects of our world evolve in the next 25 years and what could this mean for humanity?

How Might Our World Change in the Next 25 Years?

The notion of what constitutes a very human future might evolve quite dramatically over the next 25 years. Over that period, many different fields of science and technology will progress at an exponential rate or faster and combine to create currently unimaginable possibilities. At the same time, we will see these developments have a dramatic impact on and be influenced by the complex interactions of societal norms and behaviors, economic thinking, geo-politics, and notions of business, work, and employment. Here we explore some snapshot scenarios of how these factors might all play out and interact over the next 25 years.

The Stuff of Life

Artificial Living–Unless there's a dramatic slowdown or reversal in technological progress, it is reasonable to suggest that artificial intelligence (AI) will permeate our lives and our world. The technology will be in use across every aspect of society from healthcare and education to entertainment and financial services. Smart systems could manage our social lives, help us select the ideal partners for dating, marriage, and reproduction, monitor our health in liaison with our doctors, and personalize our education so content is delivered in the way we learn best.

The technology will likely be making legal decisions in court, determining our benefit payments, fact checking politicians, and powering the transport sector. For some, AI will be seen to be uplifting humanity and creating powerful new possibilities to enhance life and the way it is lived. For others, the concern will be that technology has stripped us of identity, purpose, agency, and privacy.

Aging–Science and technology advances associated with human longevity mean that people are expected to be living longer and healthier lives than ever before. Experts believe that organs will be regenerated in vitro and implanted with 100% success rates, similar to plugging new devices into 20th-century computers. Unlimited stem cells could be used to grow or repair any type of organ, in vitro or in situ. Transplant rejection should no longer be an issue, and with the exception of the brain, literally all of our organs should be replaceable by new synthetic, grown or printed ones.

Intelligent nano-robots could help with the diagnosis and treatment of diseases at any age, including pre-birth surgery. They will be able to read from and write into our biology. They should also be able to detect and destroy neoplasms, thus holding out the prospect of defeating cancer forever. Similar to nano-robots, the expectation is that bio-computers will be inoculated into the human body to perform complex tasks, for instance sensing and monitoring the status of organs or repairing tissues and organs in real time.

Artificial Wombs–Within the next 25 years it may be possible to prevent preterm mortality in infants by use of artificial wombs that provide all the conditions required to safely achieve full development and birth of a fetus. This technology would at first be used to save at-risk pregnancies but may over time become a reproductive technology available to consumers interested in having a baby without pregnancy.

Countering Antibiotic Failure–Many pathogens are gaining immunity to the antibiotic medicines available today. Without antibiotics, common illness and medical procedures, even pregnancy and childbirth, could become life endangering events. In the next 25 years, is it possible that we will experience "the end of antibiotics" as suggested by the World Health Organization in 2016? Fortunately, the microbial threat is being met with advanced drug development, allowing medical researchers to explore new approaches to fight superbugs. New strategies on the horizon range from genetic modification of germs and implantable semiconductors through to the discovery of new antibacterial agents in soil.

Transhumanism–Over the next 25 years, Information and Communications Technologies (ICTs) and bio-medicine could fundamentally improve the human condition and greatly enhance human intellectual, physical, and psychological capacities. As a result, the notion of the "transhuman" could emerge. For example, the augmentation of human beings' cognitive and intellectual abilities through technological implants, such as memory storage, is a process that is well underway already. These enhancements mean humans could achieve heightened senses and biological capabilities that are so far the prerogative of other species (e.g. speed, resistance, adaptation to extreme conditions, etc.). Conversely, future cyborgs and soft robots could be built out of biological components. For some this is simply the next stage in our evolution and the ultimate way to preserve humanity. For others there are a variety of concerns around the moral and religious implications of such developments. There are also questions of who might be able to afford such augmentations and the further polarization of society.

Sustaining Humanity

Water–As climate change continues to alter rainfall patterns worldwide, water may become an increasingly scarce resource. Regions with the financial capital may be able to invest in the latest microfiltration technologies, thus allowing constant recycling of waste water into drinkable water. Desalination plants may be the solution in arid regions along coastlines. Hopefully, as technology improves, and costs fall, the issues associated with desalination, namely high energy usage and residual salt, could be resolved to such a degree that coastal regions all over the world would be able to afford desalination. Access to plentiful clean water could have dramatic impacts on health, migration patterns, agriculture, and even interstate conflicts.

Agricultural Disruption and a Food Revolution–Within the next 25 years every aspect of the food ecosystem we know could change. The food chain will undergo a major transformation led by AI. Fruits and vegetables might be grown in buildings controlled by AI rather than on farms, meat could be cloned, and we might see widespread consumption of 3D printed food. Food innovation will see the rise of vertical farming and lab grown meat. Hydroponic plants, fruits, and vegetables might change agriculture as we know it, and help revolutionize the food industry. Population growth and city expansions are having major consequences, driving a lack of growing space and food in many parts of the world. The growing global population will force us to find creative solutions. Having AI-controlled hydroponic vertical farms on the sides of buildings might be one of the solutions.

Artificial Meat–In-vitro cloned meat could be another future solution to our food supply problems. While lab grown meat may still face many challenges, such as flavor control, it also has many advantages such as less waste, less risk of viruses, reduced space requirements, lower emissions, and reduced environmental impacts, among others. These benefits seem to outweigh the disadvantages and drawback of traditionally reared livestock. The idea of artificial meat might disturb us, nonetheless this solution seems to be finding its way into our diets.

Technology in Service of Humanity

Smarter Money–By combining the power of AI and blockchain, the concept of money could evolve into electronic tokens with far more types of assets tradeable within the one "currency." For example, we might earn tokens from our employment, as rewards from retailers and airlines, and as micro-credits for completing workplace training, school learning tasks, or community service actions. Instead of simply liking a track from a musician, we could now make a micro-payment to them with a fraction of a token. State or community funded tokens could also be given to acknowledge the value of the tasks undertaken by family members performing home care tasks that have traditionally gone unrewarded such as caring for children, the elderly, and the ill. This evolution from cash and cryptocurrencies toward a universal means of exchange could mean the end of cash and foreign exchange markets. Broadening the means of paying for goods and services could allow people to realize the full value of their various dormant assets, such as airline loyalty points, and help address social exclusion.

Art, Sciences, and Humanities–The challenges facing humanity are revealing themselves as increasingly global and highly interconnected. The next few decades should give us the tools to start mastering this complexity in terms of a deeper understanding, but also in terms of policy and action with more predictability of impacts. This will result from a combination of an exponentially increasing volume of data from various sources of evidence (smart grids, mobility data, sensor data, socio-economic data) along with the rise of AI, dynamic modeling, and new visualization, analysis, and synthesis techniques (like narrative). It will also rely on a new alliance between science and society.

Hyperconnectivity–The prevailing connectivity scenario that underpins most government, business, and technology sector thinking for the next 25 years is that the internet and its distributed successors will continue to expand as global connectors, enabled by advances in underlying technologies (e.g. blockchain, transmission protocols, photonic networks, quantum and organic computing, etc.) and by the need to support more and more sophisticated application scenarios bridging the physical and virtual worlds instantaneously. The complexity and significance of the internet should increase dramatically as we move to the new era of nano sensors and devices, and of virtual spaces and 3D social networks exchanging zillions of bytes of data every day.

Media Evolution–Social media and its successors will continue the process of replacing traditional editorial media as the dominant news and information platform over the next 25 years. The evidence is already accumulating: people like to curate their own lives through social media. As new cohorts of youth enter the digital arena, they become ever-more expert in creating their own user-generated content—dramatizing and exploiting it through social media. Scarcity of attention means less time for editorial media and fewer resources allocated to it. The means of delivery will also expand to include personalized content in multiple media and potentially event direct uploads to our brains. For many, this evolution is seen as a process of democratizing creation and access and breaks the control of those who would seek to dictate what news and content we consume. Others will remain concerned over fake news, bias, and the potential for reader manipulation.

Business, Work, and Talent

New Production Models–In 20-30 years the world's economy may change significantly, driven by the advent of new technological and societal innovations and the industries they enable. Advanced robotics, AI, automation, and smart manufacturing could bring most of today's production back to a local sustainable dimension. Continued evolution of 3D and 4D printers should make possible the self-production of many consumer items like clothes or furniture. Ultimately, only large artifacts (e.g. aircraft) may still be produced in centralized plants.

Cradle-to-Grave Work and Play–In 20-30 years, healthcare advances should enable people to work throughout their extended lifespan and change jobs according to varying personal needs and aspirations. The idea of the steady, permanent job is predicted to become a relic of the 20th century. Under such a scenario, perhaps only a minority of the population will still experience linear/sequential life cycles (i.e. study - job - family

- retirement). We could see a situation where health and wellbeing have improved to such an extent that citizens could do what they like, irrespective of their age. Technology is expected to continue transforming the very nature of work and the dynamics of organizations and labor markets. For instance, part-time work, teleworking, virtual meetings etc. may become common practices at all levels long before 2050.

Learning–The future education and learning landscape will be characterized by an increased "blurring of boundaries" between the different levels and directions of education, between schools, higher education, and industry. This evolving education ecosystem should provide greater flexibility in designing educational pathways tailored to individual needs and combining several education modalities into a lifelong and stimulating learning experience. Technology is increasingly supporting new forms of learning, for instance using virtual spaces and enhanced classrooms for experimentation and full immersion in learning settings not achievable otherwise. Over time these will likely include ever-more powerful simulations, intelligent conversational agents, and brain-to-machine or even brain-to-brain interfaces.

The Global Agenda

Global Governance–The current outlook for many observers and analysts is dominated by the hard and soft tensions that surround us, ranging from long-standing military conflicts and terrorism through to trade wars and sanctions. However, many shifts are possible in a 25-year time frame. Societies could be characterized by continuous interplay between individual and collective interests—potentially leading to tensions between two opposing models: 1) a society where only a few decide for all, either as elected representatives, or because new forms of oligarchic power emerge to exert societal manipulation; and 2) a society with neither classes nor hierarchies, characterized by participatory leadership and new forms of "chaordic" organization, where all have the possibility to co-decide on most if not all issues that matter to them.

Asia Rising—Looking at the development of the Asian market, we can expect that within 25 years world economic and industrial leadership will have passed to China and India. The growth of China and other Asian economies will continue to outstrip more developed nations and see Asian nations establish themselves as the driving force of the world economy rather than the USA and European countries.

Global People and Power—In the coming 20-30 years, our increasingly hyperconnected and immersive lives should enable people to be more empowered than ever to share knowledge, become aware of their environment, and take informed and responsible decisions. Such developments will allow us all to become active players in the global scene. New platforms for social networking could allow citizens to self-organize into communities that emerge as new powers able to exert influence and address shared problems in a more structured, responsible, and concurrent manner.

Societal Infrastructures

City Powerhouses—A number of cities will grow into megacities, which have the potential to be highly vascularized by eco-friendly and energy-sustainable transportation modes and filled with new dwellings and buildings made from innovative construction materials. If current trends continue, then all elements of the city will be connected to a higher supra-network, the future internet, on which a whole new service-economy would thrive—the so-called "internet of everyone." In this vision, cities throughout Europe would compete among each other as places to be, developing their own forms of participatory citizenship to drive a continuous co-creation of the cityscape and its multi-cultural social fabric.

Autonomous City Centers—Following increasingly widely invoked policy moves to ban petrol and diesel fueled vehicles from city centers in the coming years, the same could happen with manually driven cars. We are entering an era that will be marked by exponential innovation changing ideas of asset ownership, delivering radical leaps forward in AI, providing increasingly efficient electric propulsion units for vehicles, and enabling the emergence of genuinely smart city infrastructures. These relatively smooth transitions should lead to other changes in cities, including the removal of redundant traffic signals and the remodeling of some street intersections. The clear benefits for humanity here would include cleaner, more livable, safer cities.

Autonomous Commuter Trains–Overground and subway/metro commuter services are now fully automated in many cities. At busier stations and at peak travel times, train staff supervise the safety of passengers at the station, but the trains themselves are fully autonomous with AI systems driving the train and monitoring passengers. As yet, long distance express trains retain on-board crews, although much like civilian aircraft, the drivers' roles are to supervise the systems and provide on-board customer service. The move to autonomous trains might allow for a more predictable service that wouldn't be affected by issues such as staff illness or recruitment issues. Others might be concerned that this is another development that will see net job loss.

Autonomous Cargo Aircraft–While most passengers are skeptical about an autonomous plane ride to their destination in the sun, cargo has no such qualms. While regulations allow the operation of autonomous aircraft for cargo purposes, they are still operated between specialist cargo hub airports, separate from passenger traffic. There would of course be serious implications for those who lose their jobs. One view is that the move to autonomous cargo might help free up trained pilots to service the expected growth of passenger demand for air transport and the associated shortage of flight crew. Clearly many would also be concerned about the environmental impacts of an overall growth in aviation.

The First 3D Printed Moon Base–Following a series of missions in the coming years to create an autonomous 3D accommodation manufacturing facility on the Moon's surface, the facility should be ready within 25 years. The Moon base would support greater and more extensive autonomous and human exploration of the Moon's surface and serve as a base for onward missions to deep space. There are an increasing number of people raising concerns over the Earth's capacity to sustain a growing population and over the potentially irrevocable environmental damage that results from human activity. Some see the establishment of settlements on other planets as a way of reducing the pressures here on Earth and providing alternative habitats for humanity. Some might see these as only accessible by the ultra-wealthy.

Scenarios as a Tool of Dialogue and Exploration

Stepping ahead 25 years allows us to break the shackles of current assumptions and constraining beliefs to explore new possibilities and stimulate constructive dialogue. In many cases those scenarios posit a better future for most of humanity. However, there are a number from the use of AI to transhumanism which will polarize views, and in many cases, it is hard to see a coming together on one global perspective. Indeed, there are relatively few issues today where we could claim global support for a particular desired future.

- *Which scenarios offer the most positive outlook for humanity from your perspective?*
- *How can citizens best engage in shaping the future when so many of the developments and shaping factors seem to lie out of our control?*
- *What new global mechanisms might be required to steer a future path that protects the interests of people and the planet?*

This article is based on Fast Future's contribution to the European Commission Futurium platform, and interviews given to Best Life and MSN.

Harnessing Technological Bursts of Possibility

Steve Wells, Rohit Talwar, and Alexandra Whittington

How can we harness technological opportunity to invent the businesses and jobs of the future?

Understanding the Drivers of Change

A critical part of ensuring a very human future is ensuring we understand and deploy the technologies that are reshaping our world. In this article we explore some of the technologies that are disrupting our world, the new industries and job opportunities they will enable, and the vital roles of foresight and people-centric thinking in ensuring a viable future of our firms and our people.

Business in a Transformative Context

Everywhere we look, we see physical world mindsets and beliefs colliding with those of the digital world. Physical world people and businesses tend to focus on things they can see, touch, and manufacture. Even when their output exists largely in digital form (e.g. legal contracts) they still think of their world in very tangible terms. They are often comfortable with things they are familiar with, tend to think of progress in incremental ways, typically see technology as an enabler and cost center, and rarely see themselves as technology businesses.

Those born of or living in the digital world tend to be more data-centric, comfortable with technology, and are often early adopters of new technology, having grown up with social media, electronic devices, and virtual communications. When they look at the world or an industry, they see the data and information first and look for ways to leverage the data and to streamline systems solutions. They focus on outcomes and believe that—from vehicle manufacture to curing world hunger—the problem is at heart one that can be solved by technology-enabled redesign of the entire system, not just by human brain power and incremental improvement. Their view is that the application of science and new technologies are the way to both develop solutions to existing problems, and to capitalizing on emerging opportunities.

Technology's "Possibility Explosion"

We are seeing a "possibility explosion" from exponential science and technology developments. Not only that, we are seeing the potential of the combinational impact of technologies that are being developed in tandem, for example artificial intelligence (AI) and robotics. What we know about these technologies is that they will drive dramatic and rapid change in society, across industries, and in the domains of business, leisure, government, healthcare, and education.

In this environment, the boundaries between magic and science are blurring. There are some radical developments taking place, many of which we will see come to fruition during our working lives such as mapping and uploading the human brain, and cognitive, genetic, physical, and electronic enhancement of the human body. These radical developments—particularly when put together with AI—could create challenging ethical dilemmas should machines gain self-awareness and even emotional intelligence.

We don't have to look very far into the past to see the transformative impact of combinational technology developments. Although the pace of change is accelerating, transformation in information and communication technologies (ICT) has been occurring for some years, so we have an evolutionary model we can look to. Think of the computer; from bus-sized machines in air-conditioned rooms, to the desktop, the laptop, and the tablet. Now consider the parallel development of the telephone, from the desktop to the "luggable" mobile, devices with apps, and now the smartphone. Just think for a second how transformative smartphones alone have been, how they have become part of the fabric of our daily life, and how we take for granted the ability to access information, communicate, and be entertained on the move. The following examples demonstrate some of the exponential possibilities that are on the horizon in the aftermath of the most recent technological bursts of progress.

Brain-Computer Interface (BCI)–This is a direct communication pathway between an enhanced or wired brain and an external device. A BCI is often directed at researching, mapping, assisting, augmenting, or repairing human cognitive or sensory-motor functions, but their application could also extend to "mind control" of objects and devices.

Wearables and Implants–These and near body devices are coming into play. Many are currently being used for health and sports perfor-mance monitoring but increasingly we see wearable technology for other uses; Google's Glasses and the Apple watch being just two examples. Soon, we will see device recharge technology built into clothing fabrics, conductive fibers woven into fabric that provide processing capacity for wearable devices, and GPS tracking devices fitted into shoes. We are already used to some implants: heart pace-makers, cochlear implants, and ocular implants, for example. But a new range of implants will help to enhance other body functions into the future including memory for our electronic devices. Some of these technologies are being patented now.

Augmented and Virtual Reality (AR/VR)–These look set to play increasingly significant roles as we seek ever-more immersive expe-riences. A growing range of devices, surfaces, and appliances in our homes, offices, factories, and schools will be connected—creating the so-called Internet of Things (IoT)—and we will see new ways to interact with information. Estimates vary widely, but within ten years there could be between 200 billion and a trillion devices and objects connected to the internet, all capable of exchanging information and providing different sorts of AR/VR functionality and experiences. Video and projection technologies will improve, including holographic technologies that will allow us to share information in new ways.

Autonomous Vehicles–A number of experiments are taking place on public roads across the world, and while cars have been the focus of much media attention, lorries, buses, trains, ships, and planes are all subject to developments in autonomous/driverless technology.

3D/4D Printing–These provide the opportunity to distribute production to where it's needed and at significantly reduced costs. Why would you manufacture products thousands of miles away from the market and transport them, if instead you can make them where the consumer is?

Artificial Intelligence (AI)–This is arguably the big game changer and becoming more commonplace. We already see narrow AI in use in internet searches, customer targeting applications, and in predictive analytics. But AI has much greater capability that will emerge into every aspect of our lives in the near future. Increasingly devices will learn more about us, help to provide decision support to us, and take on more of our tasks. We are automating ever-larger amounts of human social and workplace activity and that is set to continue at an accelerated pace.

The Future of Business

At Fast Future, we have identified six high value industry clusters that we expect to be radically impacted or enabled by exponential and combinatorial technology developments. Indeed, each underlying sector within each cluster is expected to be worth US$1Tn or more by 2025:

1. Information and communications technologies (including, AI, robotics, and blockchain)

2. Production and construction systems (From 3D/4D printing and synthetic biology to rapid, green and sustainable construction approaches)
3. Citizen services and domestic infrastructure (from health and elder care to smart vehicles and new education approaches)
4. New societal infrastructure and services (encompassing intelligent transport, the sharing economy, and smart cities)
5. Industry transformation (the modernizations of sectors such as financial services, accounting, and legal)
6. Energy and environment (from renewables and fracking to environmental protection and repair).

These technological advances will have an impact right across society and all business sectors, fundamentally changing many. For those that doubt the possible scale of impact, there are a number of prominent recent examples where established businesses have suffered because they ignored the signals sent by new market entrants, new technologies, and new business models. For example, Kodak ignored new digital photography market entrants and were over-confident in their brand and their customer loyalty. As a result, their market share declined rapidly, and they rejected a technology innovation of their own invention—the digital camera. The company emerged from Chapter 11 bankruptcy protection in 2013 and is now a very different business.

Similarly, in 2000 the relative new entrant Netflix proposed a partnership with Blockbuster. The suggestion was that Netflix would run Blockbuster's brand online, and Blockbuster would promote Netflix in stores. Netflix's advantages were lower costs and greater product variety. Having turned down the Netflix overtures, Blockbuster were unable or unwilling to alter their business model and went bankrupt in 2010, while Netflix has market capitalization of over $150 billion at the time of writing.

Conversely, other companies have embraced the opportunity to deploy technology to develop products and services that put the customer at the heart of the operation. Uber was founded as a consumer-centric transportation company that utilized licensed taxi drivers for ridesharing services. The basis of what we see today was the integration of a mobile application to connect passengers with drivers of vehicles for hire within a specified geographical area. What differentiated Uber from hundreds of other taxi apps was a more customer-oriented experience including the ability to track their vehicle as it is on route to them, driver rating, and new payment options including fare sharing between multiple occupants. Uber is disrupting the market for taxi cabs and transportation in general and has already expanded into home delivery, food, and helicopter services. It is also exploring driverless cars, drone delivery, and on-demand urban air transportation.

In the hospitality sector, Airbnb offers a user-friendly site for discovering and booking accommodation. The curated listings offer consumers far more than just "renting a spare room." The proposition is about discovering cool, quirky, and creative properties. Rentals are generally 30-80% lower than available hotels. For the property owner, it is free to list with Airbnb who charge a 3% fee to process payments. Guests pay a service fee to Airbnb. They too have potential to transform a traditional service model—accommodation and space rental.

Harnessing Exponentiality for a Very Human Future

Moore's Law has shown that $1,000 worth of computing power will double in capability every 18-24 months. If we apply that to the processing power of existing computers, in seven years or so we will see computers 128 times more powerful than today. Organizations that can develop the appropriate mindset and apply this notion of exponentiality could develop thriving business propositions and achieve dramatic growth.

Indeed, many organizations are trying to bring exponential ideas into their thinking. They are asking if technology can radically change what they do, and what they can change to solve more problems faster, deliver quicker, and dramatically reduce process times. In short, they are using exponential thinking approaches to change the way they look at problems, solutions, and opportunities. They are changing the personality of their organization, posing the question, "Should we play by the rules of the game or change the game itself?" They recognize that staying still—taking no action—is normally tantamount to going backward. We advocate moving forward into a very human future.

- *How does your organization approach the assessment of new and potentially disruptive technologies?*
- *What are your customers saying about how they see technology disrupting their businesses and how might that impact your firm?*
- *Which technologies hold the most potential to redefine the way your sector operates; what might the new business models look like?*

A version of this chapter was originally published in HR Review under the title "Technology is Giving Us Bursts of Possibility—Is Your Organization Ready?"

The Future Evolution of Artificial Intelligence

Rohit Talwar, Steve Wells, Alexandra Whittington, Helena Calle, and
April Koury

What are the core stages in the future development of artificial
intelligence and how might its application evolve over the next 20
years?

Beyond Hysteria

"Artificial intelligence (AI) is coming to get us" and it's just a small step
from a self-driving car to AIs taking over our world and the "end of
days" dystopias that Hollywood has popularized in a number of recent
films. Or so some would have us believe. The reality is far less dramatic,
and AI will need to go through a number of stages of development
before it reaches the most extreme scenarios—if ever. In our recent
book *Beyond Genuine Stupidity—Ensuring AI Serves Humanity*, we
explore the possibilities and challenges presented by this game-changing technology. In this chapter we draw on key concepts from the
book to demystify the fundamentals of AI, provide insights into seven
possible stages through which it might develop, and highlight the types
of applications we might see in the next 15-20 years.

What is Artificial Intelligence and Why Now?

At the core of the concept of AI is the idea of developing intelligent machines—e.g. computer algorithms that work and react like humans. Applications include performing speech recognition, natural language processing and translation, visual perception, learning, reasoning, inference, strategizing, planning, intuition, and decision-making. People have been working on these concepts since the 1940s and AI has experienced many false dawns, or "winters" as the AI community likes to describe them.

This time around, the feeling is that AI is here to stay and that it could become central to every aspect of human existence from detecting and treating heart failure through to running companies, economies, and legal systems. There are five main factors that have made AI the hot topic on the agenda for companies, investors, politicians, and citizens alike. Firstly, we are seeing the development of far more efficient and smarter machine learning and neural network tools—the core algorithms through which AI systems develop their intelligence. In parallel, computer hardware processing power and transaction speeds have accelerated, and cloud computing allows us to share and combine data and processing power across the globe. At the same time companies such as Google and Amazon have amassed vast amounts of data that require AI to process it—giving rise to the fifth factor—money. The scale of the opportunity presented by AI has seen billions of dollars being invested by these new technology companies, corporates in other sectors, venture funded start-ups, and governments—so the game is well and truly on.

Core Fields of Artificial Intelligence

There are a number of different fields which fall under the broad umbrella of AI; the main ones are described below. The most common are rule-based or "expert" systems which can apply a vast number of rules on a consistent basis. These have been around for over 30 years with common applications including the processing of loans and mortgage applications and basic medical diagnosis. Robotic Process Automation (RPA) is the next stage on, with machines performing complete processes that in the past required a combination of rule-based decision-making and an element of human judgment. These are common in tasks such as handling calls to service centers, processing an insurance claim, or checking the calculations in an architectural design.

Tasks considered closer to true human intelligence include voice recognition, interpretation of human conversations conducted in "natural" languages, and speech generation. Similarly, considerable progress has been made with computer vision—enabling the ever-more accurate recognition of images—with applications as diverse as spotting misshapen pies on a production line through to facial recognition for airport security purposes. Other increasingly deployed AI applications include tools that can undertake sophisticated planning, scheduling, and optimization of tasks—encompassing everything from manufacturing to air crew rostering.

The hottest field of AI at present is machine learning—the notion of using statistical techniques to help systems learn from data. This is taken a stage further by the area gaining most attention at present because of its potential—namely the use of neural networks and deep learning algorithms to develop systems with learning capabilities closer to those of the human brain. These tools are being used across a range of applications, with the most common being chatbots to perform increasingly sophisticated customer interaction tasks by combining machine learning, natural language processing, and speech generation. Finally, robotics is being put to widespread use in everything from warehouse management and surgery to cooking burgers in restaurants. Robots typically combine a number of the other AI fields to provide smart mechanoids.

Seven Stages in the Future Evolution of Artificial Intelligence

With literally hundreds of thousands of developers and data scientists across the planet now working on AI, the pace of development is accelerating, with increasingly eye-catching breakthroughs being announced on a daily basis. This has also led to a lot of confusion about what we can do with AI today and what might be possible at some point in the future. To provide some clarity on the possible development path, we outline the seven distinct stages in the evolution of AI's capabilities that we could envisage over time.

*Stage 1–Rule-Based Systems–*These now surround us in everything from business software (RPA) and domestic appliances through to aircraft autopilots. They are the most common manifestations of AI in the world today.

*Stage 2–Context Awareness and Retention–*These algorithms build up a body of information about the specific domain they are being applied in. They are trained on the knowledge and experience of the best humans, and their knowledge base can be updated as new situations and queries arise. The most common manifestations include chatbots—often used in frontline customer enquiry handling—and the "roboadvisors" that are helping with everything from suggesting the right oil for your motorbike through to providing investment advice.

*Stage 3–Domain Specific Expertise–*These systems can develop expertise in a specific domain that extends beyond the capability of humans because of the sheer volume of information they can access to make each decision. We have seen their use in applications such as cancer diagnosis. Perhaps the most commonly cited example is Google Deepmind's AlphaGo. The system was given a set of learning rules and the objective of winning and then it taught itself how to play Go with human support to nudge it back on course when it made poor decisions. Go reportedly has more moves than there are atoms in the universe—so you cannot teach it in the same way as you might with a chess playing program. In March 2016, AlphaGo defeated the 18-time world Go champion Lee Sedol by four games to one.

The following year, AlphaGo Zero was created, and given no guidance or human support at all. Equipped only with its learning rules, AlphaGo Zero watched thousands of Go games and developed its own game-playing strategies. After three days, it took on AlphaGo and won by 100 games to nil. Such applications are an example of what is possible when machines can acquire human-scale intelligence. However, at present they are limited to one domain. So, currently AlphaGo Zero would forget what it knows about playing Go if you started to teach it how to spot fraudulent transactions in an accounting audit.

Stage 4–Reasoning Machines–These algorithms have a "theory of mind"—some ability to attribute mental states to themselves and others, for example they have an understanding of the notions of beliefs, intentions, knowledge, and how their own logic works. Hence, they have the capacity to reason, negotiate, and interact with humans and other machines. Such algorithms are currently at the development stage, but we can expect to see them in commercial applications in the next few years.

Stage 5–Self-Aware Systems / Artificial General Intelligence (AGI)– This is the goal of many working in the AI field—creating systems with human-like intelligence. No such applications are in evidence today, however, some say we could see them in as little as five years, while others believe we may never truly achieve this level of machine intelligence. There are many examples of AGI in the popular media ranging from HAL the ship computer in *2001 A Space Odyssey*, to the "Synths" in the television series *Humans*. For decades now, writers and directors have tried to convey a world where the machines can function at a similar level to humans. Some argue that while the machines may display human-like intelligence, this will still just be their algorithms at play and that they will not actually be intelligent in the way humans would understand the term.

Stage 6–Artificial Superintelligence (ASI)–This is the notion of developing AI algorithms that are capable of outperforming the smartest of humans in every domain. Clearly, it is hard to articulate what the capabilities might be of something that exceeds human intelligence, but we could imagine ASI solving current world problems such as hunger and dangerous climate change. Such systems might also invent new fields of science, redesign economic systems, and evolve wholly new models of governance. Again, expert views vary as to when and whether such a capability might ever be possible, but few think we will see it in the next decade. Films like *Her* and *Ex Machina* provide interesting depictions of the possibilities in a world where our technology might outsmart us.

***Stage 7–Singularity and Transcendence*–**This is the notion that the exponential development path enabled by ASI could lead to a massive expansion in human capability. We might one day be sufficiently augmented and enhanced such that humans could connect our brains to each other and to a future successor of the current internet. This "hive mind" would allow us to share ideas, solve problems collectively, and even give others access to our dreams as observers or participants. Taking things a stage further, we might also transcend the limits of the human body and connect to other forms of intelligence on the planet—animals, plants, weather systems, and the natural environment. Some proponents such as Ray Kurzweil, Google's Director of Engineering, suggest that we could see the Singularity happen by 2045 as a result of exponential rates of progress across a range of science and technology disciplines. Others argue fervently that it is simply impossible and that we will never be able to capture and digitize human consciousness.

Envisioning a Smarter World

To help bring to life how these developments might impact our world and what a smarter future might look like, below we have outlined a possible development timeline for AI over the next 20 years or so:

Now to 2020

- Instantaneous real-time translation
- Intelligence built into the machines, sensors, and objects that surround us
- Self-editing software
- Fully automated decentralized autonomous organizations (DAO)—smart corporations with no employees
- Artificial intelligence adopted by most firms either deliberately or unknowingly through the applications they rent or purchase

- Personal device based intelligent agents manage our lives and guard our data (e.g. Siri+++++)
- Swarm robotics—groups of robots combining and self-managing themselves to complete a task such as an environmental clean-up, bridge repair, or building construction.

2021-2025

- Between 70% and 90% of all initial customer interactions are likely to be conducted or managed by AI
- Product development in a range of sectors from fashion items and consumer goods to manufacturing equipment could increasingly be undertaken and tested by AI
- Individuals will be able to define and design the personalized products and services they require in sectors ranging from travel through to banking, savings, and insurance
- The technology is likely to be deployed across all government agencies and legal systems—with only the most complex cases requiring a human judge and full court proceedings
- Autonomous vehicles will start appearing in many cities across the world
- Our intelligent assistants could now be managing large parts of our lives from travel planning through to compiling the information we need prior to a meeting.

2026-2035+

- Globally approved, smart crypto tokens may be accepted alongside fiat currencies as we edge toward a single global medium of exchange
- Artificial intelligence is likely to have penetrated every commercial sector
- The evolution of AI could see the emergence of a wide range of fully automated DAO businesses including banks, travel agents, and insurance companies
- Scientific breakthroughs could enable us to develop artificial animal and ecosystem intelligence

- The emergence of self-aware and self-replicating software systems and robots
- There is a reasonable possibility of achieving Artificial General Intelligence
- There is a small chance of creating Artificial Superintelligence
- The Singularity remains an unlikely possibility in this time frame.

Conclusion–Preparing for a Smarter World

The pace of AI development seems likely to continue and we can expect to see regular breakthroughs that blow our collective minds. However, we shouldn't assume a smooth progression through the seven stages of AI outlined above. Moving from reasoning systems to AGI isn't equivalent to the exponential progression we have become accustomed to in computer power, memory storage, and internet connection speeds. To reach those final three stages of AI, massive breakthroughs are required in areas such as neuroscience, understanding consciousness, neural networks, and deep learning algorithms.

What is clear is that, over the next 15-20 years, our world is likely to experience several fundamental transformations as this "Fourth Industrial Revolution" powered by smart machines touches every nation, life, and sector on the planet. The critical priority and challenge is ensuring that these advances don't progress unchecked and render humans irrelevant. We have to establish governance frameworks and a public voice that are strong enough to guide the development of AI in service of humanity not in place of it.

- *How do you view the potential of AI in society?*
- *How might the fabric of our world change if we achieve AGI or ASI?*
- *Should the Singularity be realized, what might it be like to share our thoughts and dreams?*

A version of this chapter was originally published in Enterprise Management 360 under the title "The 7 Stages of the Future Evolution of Artificial Intelligence."

Disrupting the Future for the Better—20 Robotics and Connected Devices that Could Impact Our Future Lives

Rohit Talwar, Steve Wells, Alexandra Whittington, April Koury, and Maria Romero

How might the next wave of disruptive technologies change our notions of everyday life and "normal"?

Harnessing Tomorrow's Technology in Service of Humanity

In our two most recent books, *Beyond Genuine Stupidity—Ensuring AI Serves Humanity* and *The Future Reinvented—Reimagining Life, Society, and Business*, we explored how we can harness the potential of artificial intelligence (AI), robotics, and a growing range of other increasingly powerful technologies in service of humanity. Here we highlight examples of how robotics and connected devices in particular could change a range of life experiences—hopefully for the better.

If we could time travel 5, 15, or 20 years into the future, what would we see? It doesn't take a team of futurists to imagine a continuing evolution of intelligent, robotic, connected, digital, and social technology innovations persisting for decades to come. Design qualities such as automated, smart, digitized, and autonomous are likely to define the future tools we'll see across key societal domains such as business, manufacturing, retail, service, agriculture, military, healthcare, leisure, entertainment, homecare, and even sexbots. At the same time, we have to be concerned that constant surveillance, "technological omniscience," and "control at a distance" are some of the key features of the coming waves of gadgetry that could put seemingly god-like powers into the hands of mere mortals.

In practice, reality is never as mythical or perfect as we might imagine or desire. While exciting hyper-efficient and near magical macro images of the high-tech future captivate us, it is essential to stay grounded about the future as it might be experienced by the individual. Indeed, something that is less readily explored among most future predictions is a depiction of the way that disruptive technologies may actually affect daily life in the future, for example once they become normalized and somewhat taken for granted.

Across all our work at Fast Future, in our books, articles, and speeches, we have focused on a core theme of how we can and should retain humanity in the face of disruptive technology. This chapter explores the various ways that robotic and connected devices could disrupt the future of day-to-day life for the better. In our view, envisioning the possible products and services of the future means standing in the shoes of the people who would use them—not as fictional characters, but as real people with similar problems, dilemmas, emotions, relationships, and challenges to those we have today.

Understanding and seeing hypothetical future customers and employees as people experiencing some of the same universal human dramas that we do today, the future feels a little more relatable. Below is an excerpt from one of our futurist mind melds exploring 20 possible robotic and connected devices that might impact our lives between today and 2040.

Robotics

1. *Personal Drone Security*—Small drones may fly around a person's property, constantly monitoring and guarding against security

threats like trespassers or burglars. Additionally, they would alert owners of their guests' arrivals, and be able to confirm the guests' identities through video and facial recognition software.

2. *Autonomous Cars*–Self-owning independent taxis will earn fares for each ride, sharing revenue with those who manufacture, service, and refuel them. The cars would work in self-managing, self-insuring networks—covering each other in the event of increasingly rare incidents. As autonomous technology grows ever smarter, accidents will only tend to arise when human-driven vehicles are in collision with autonomous cars.

3. *Rescue Drones*–Drones are already available that can target individuals in need of emergency assistance, and either airlift them to safety or provide them with vital life-saving equipment. These drones will become ever-more sophisticated and capable, with the ability to undertake more complex search and rescue missions and perform a growing range of medical procedures on the spot.

4. *Autonomous Drones Monitoring and Repairing Infrastructure*–Constant status monitoring via connected sensors and use of autonomous repair-bots may allow for continuous and pre-emptive upkeep of physical infrastructure. As soon as a sensor detects a pothole or crack in a bridge, the appropriately skilled fleet of autonomous maintenance drones and robots could be dispatched to repair the bridge before further damage can occur. A step on from pre-planned maintenance routines could be fully autonomous inspection drones. Equipped with AI-enabled technology, they would observe and report back on the target infrastructure: power lines, railway lines, hyperloop evacuated tubes, tunnels, and bridges. Links to automated or manual repair and maintenance teams would provide information to enable timely deployment of the correct repair assets.

5. *Autonomous Drones for Crowd Control and Border Security*–Autonomous drones with AI-enabled behavior recognition and infrared capabilities could patrol border areas and other sensitive security situations when there are risks to safety and the potential for social unrest. On identification of security breaches or

potential anti-social behavior, the appropriate human or automated resources could be mobilized and deployed to counter the risk.

6. *Digital Twins*–After collecting massive amounts of data about a person through connected devices, robots would be able to replicate this person's behavior and responses. In fact, your digital twin could attend a meeting for you and comment on your behalf. Your twin could also capture and summarize the entire conversation including analysis of the body language and micro-facial expressions of the other participants and then report back.

7. *Robo-Mummy*–Continuous monitoring of health indicators would allow your devices to order what you need to prevent you getting sick. Your devices would try to nudge your decision-making toward a healthier lifestyle and what's best for you.

8. *"No Strings Attached" Sex*–Future personal pleasure offerings could include customized multi-sensory virtual reality (VR) experiences coupled with sophisticated sex toys to enhance the range of multi-sensory sensations for the user. Over time the technology will advance such that the AI personality of your digital partners could be transferable between different sex robots and devices. Hence, your settings will be up to date in whatever interface you would like to use.

9. *Personal Robo-Delivery*–Small autonomous robots are already delivering fast food and mail—soon they could run daily errands while their owners work. As our grocery order or dry cleaning becomes ready, the robot is alerted and sets out through the town to pick up the orders from the local shops.

10. *Droneloo*–Single user droneloos could be summoned on demand—dropping into the midst of a crowd at an open-air festival, concert, public rally, or sporting event to enable those caught short to relieve themselves in privacy.

11. *Self-Filling Vertical Farmer's Market Bag*–Smart, self-filling, self-unloading, reusable bags could communicate with smart homes and smart appliances to fulfill new orders from a local vertical farm or supermarket. The bag would fill itself with groceries at the point of origin, be delivered via autonomous vehicle or drone,

unload on arrival, and be returned empty on the next delivery run. This could save time for shoppers, support local produce, and discourage food waste.

12. *A Robotic New Year's Eve in Trafalgar Square*—Autonomous ambulances with in-vehicle robots could provide immediate first aid, carrying out more complex tasks under the guidance of remote video-linked doctors. Personal drones would extract injured parties from the crowd and transport them to the ambulance. Autonomous food trucks would use drones to deliver the food to the individual wherever they stand without having to leave their spot.

13. *Robotic Farming*—Our farms may become entirely automated. Intelligent robots would plan, plant, water, weed, fertilize, and harvest entire crops at the perfect time based on a continuous feed of connected sensor information. An apple at a grocery store may never have been touched by a human hand until the moment a customer picks it from the shelf or eats what their robo-assistant has selected.

Connected Devices

14. *Life Automation*—Connected devices and "life automation" apps could share your agenda and habits to plan the flow of your day. Music from your surround system would automatically keep playing in your headphones after you leave your home and switch to the in-car system when you get behind the wheel. The home heating system would turn on when you are ten minutes away. Food would be delivered or ready to eat minutes after you walk in the front door.

15. *Never Alone*—The days when you could get off the grid are coming to an end. Although you could be physically alone, your digital footprint, assembled through all the connected devices and sensors on and in your body and around you, could reveal your whereabouts in a microsecond. While this might seem an invasion of privacy it could reassure worried parents and help

rescue workers find everyone present at the time of a fire or building collapse.

16. *Automated Sharing*–Sensors in devices and objects would identify opportunities to participate in the sharing economy, i.e. rent or loan out your stapler, motorcycle, hammock, or home for a day. Local internets and intranets could provide neighbor-to-neighbor sharing for free or via a charge included in local taxes or building fees. Robots would undertake deliveries and ensure building safety.

17. *Environmental Monitoring*–As more and more sensors are deployed, we can expect environmental monitoring to reach a new high. A person or their autonomous car may receive tailored alerts to avoid certain streets when pollution levels are slightly elevated in those areas. Walkers might receive personalized alerts to avoid specific parks as weather conditions have caused weeds to bloom that may trigger their allergies.

18. *Unisex Utility Jacket*–This totally safe and secure everyday fashion item would keep mobile devices connected using built-in chargers and a personal private data network. The jacket might also collect, convert, store, and distribute kinetic and heat energy from the wearer's body and the sun to sell back to the local power grid.

19. *Bathroom Blocker*–This personal sensor detector and signal blocker would prevent smart toilets from testing urine samples for illegal and/or enhancement drugs. It would also detect and defend against bathroom hackers looking to steal our medical identity.

20. *AI HR*–Artificial intelligence is already changing the way HR operates. Perhaps we are edging toward humanless HR with AI-powered recruitment, selection, appointment, onboarding, performance monitoring, payment (employees, contractors, gig-bots), and offboarding based on automated needs and skills matching. The smart HR could also monitor us via all our devices and detect factors such as stress levels, distraction, the

extent of social conversation we engage in, and when we are performing at our peak.

Conclusion

If we could interview our future selves, we would have many questions: What is the benefit of having a digital twin? What are the advantages (or disadvantages) of drone security? How do autonomous devices in our midst change the quality of life? What does the day-to-day implementation of biometrics feel like? Do robots do everything to feed us from farm to table? What do you consider "smart"? Does technology make life better? How is the trade-off between protecting privacy and trading it for access to smart goods and services playing out? We can only imagine what they would say.

- *How would you design a robotic or connected device with the purpose of creating positive changes in society?*
- *How can technology developers and product designers understand the future needs of people for whom they are designing?*
- *What are the most useful or useless future products you can imagine? What new or innovative features might be in demand?*

A version of this chapter was originally published in Software Testing News under the title "Will our Future Life be Impacted Positively by These Connected and Robotic Devices?"

PART 2:
Society and Social Policy

Is Automation Destined to Rewrite all Our Futures? Three Futurist Perspectives

Rohit Talwar, Steve Wells, and Alexandra Whittington

How might society need to reframe our notions of jobs and incomes in the age of automation?

A New Economic Dialogue
In this article, we explore three alternative futurist perspectives on how advances in technology could impact notions of employment, jobs, and income.

Rohit Talwar—Let's Not Wait to Find Out
Fundamental changes are taking place in the ways organizations are using technology. Many are embarking on radical digital overhauls to enable them to deliver new offerings, enhance service, improve efficiency, and increase cost competitiveness. The reality is that widescale automation will inevitably lead to job reductions across everything from mining and the manufacturing industries to transport and the legal sector.

New sectors are of course emerging and creating opportunities—but no one yet knows if they will generate enough jobs to replace those displaced by technology, or how long that might take. Some estimates suggest up to 80% of all current jobs could be digitized. New industry sectors such as laboratory grown meat, vertical farming, autonomous vehicles, and synthetic materials will be highly automated from the outset, requiring very different capabilities and a highly skilled workforce. The transition to these new roles will not be smooth for the production worker, shift manager, warehouse assistant, sales person, truck driver, or even lawyer whose jobs are at risk.

While there might be a tendency to "wait and see"—this could be calamitously risky. The change when it happens will cascade and accelerate, rapidly leaving unprepared governments and societies in a paralyzing state of shock. I believe it is far better to anticipate impending disruptions and risks and act now to start putting society on a more sustainable footing—thus ensuring it is resilient enough to cope with the risk of large-scale technological unemployment.

I believe there are five fundamental actions that forward-looking governments should be taking right now.

1. *Experimenting with Guaranteed Basic Incomes and Services*

The firms doing the job automation need customers to buy their goods and services. Hence, we see many in Silicon Valley arguing for some form of automation tax to fund the provision of universal guaranteed basic incomes (UBI) and services (UBS) to everyone in society. Some governments refuse to countenance the idea on ideological grounds because they think it reeks of communism. However, others are recognizing that something needs to be done to avoid large-scale social decline and potential citizen unrest. Hence, many countries including Finland, Germany, and Canada are undertaking UBI experiments to understand the concept, assess the social impact, measure the costs, and prepare themselves while they still have time.

2. *A Massive Expansion of Support for Start-Up Creation*

People will inevitably have to take more control of their own destiny. One way is to create their own job or small business that is far less immune to risks of technology replacing humans. A massive expansion of support for start-up creation would accelerate the rate at which people can build new businesses and generate jobs for the mentors.

3. *Research and Development in Key Knowledge Sectors*

A competitive economy demands cutting-edge innovation. A safe society requires research and development on the materials and processes that will enable that. Not all R&D lends itself to assessment based on the return on investment—some just has to be undertaken for the betterment of society. Hence, expanding research funding and the number of places is an important enabler of tomorrow's job creation.

4. *Rethinking Education at Every Level*

Success in the future will require a smart, adaptable and highly educated workforce. Indeed, many commentators and some governments anticipate that within a decade, most new jobs will require a graduate level of education as a minimum. How that is acquired may well look very different compared to today.

To survive and thrive I think everyone will need to understand both the technologies and the mindsets shaping the future. Uber and Airbnb have lots of technological competitors—their true point of difference is their mindset—a radically different way of thinking about how you deliver on customer desires without owning any assets or employing any of the service delivery staff. We also need to help people develop higher-level skills that will help them learn rapidly and transition into jobs that don't even exist today. These include collaboration, problem solving, navigating complexity, scenario thinking, and accelerated learning.

Hence, I believe we need to massively increase the provision of free adult education using existing facilities at schools and higher education institutions for delivery—most are unused in the evening. We also need to reduce pupil-teacher ratios at school level to help with personalized support—the evidence is clear on the impact. This also means looking at the charges imposed on students pursuing higher education—we need a well-educated workforce to propel the country forward—many nations are providing free degree level education. Countries like the

UK, that charge for tertiary education, need a sustainable solution that doesn't leave future generations demotivated, disillusioned, and saddled with debts that they cannot repay.

5. *Addressing the Mental Health Challenge*
Across society, the scale and severity of mental health issues is rising. Large-scale job displacement will only increase that. An enlightened approach would be to fund people to train as therapists while still working today so that they will be ready to help when the challenge becomes a major problem in 2-4 years' time.

There's clearly a cost associated with enabling all these activities, but we have to ask ourselves of what the risks and potential costs of inaction might be. A short-term saving on such expenditure could lead to a very long-term increase in the cost of funding unemployment benefits and policing a society that feels let down.

Steve Wells–A Realigning of Resources
Exponential technology development represents a possibility explosion; the possibility to create new industries, new products and services, new business models, and new occupations. Rather than displacing more jobs than it creates, it will herald the advent of a new world, one that presents the opportunity for us to commit to a very human future.

Can automation really replace—as some have predicted—around half of existing jobs? If we consider that—even within the challenging context of the disruptive nature of exponential technology development—the very same technologies will support the creation of new businesses. They will provide scope for innovative business models to bring products and services to market for a customer base who will be working in jobs that do not exist yet.

I expect to see functions such as data analysts (leveraging big data and artificial intelligence), specialized sales representatives (commercializing and articulating new product and service propositions), and senior managers and leaders (to steer companies through the upcoming change and disruption) become critically important over the coming years.

I also expect to see an increasing number of occupations comprised of skills that are not yet considered crucial to the job today. Social skills—such as persuasion, emotional intelligence, and teaching others—will be in higher demand across industries than narrow technical skills, such as programming or equipment operation and control.

This transition is not without challenges. But, with a broader re-assessment of the partnership between business, government, and society, maybe we are entering a once in a millennium opportunity to redefine society's relationship with employment. Maybe part of what we seek is the discovery of our humanity; to find time for leisure, self-improvement, spiritualty, or being with loved ones. Maybe it is time for a very human future.

Alexandra Whittington—The Social Safety Net

I take the view that machines will manufacture and distribute everything with almost no humans involved, and new businesses will be fully automated from the start. By 2040, up to 80-90% of jobs could be gone, and not be replaced with new opportunities. This only really works for humanity under the universal basic income (UBI) scenario that Elon Musk and others have advocated for.

In 20 years, automation may have created a society where jobs aren't available or not being created at the scale necessary to employ the large numbers of people automated out of a job. Only the most highly skilled human workers would be needed, creating a huge underclass of people with no job, no prospects, and no income.

One way to pay for this program would be to fine companies for each job they automate, or to tax the use of robotic workers. In manufacturing, a form of community profit sharing could be adopted. Companies might be expected to supplement the living standards of the local communities in which they are located by providing for the basic needs of the residents and former employees. Manufacturers might go from being a profit focused business to providing a social service—giving away free products to local citizens or actual cash payments to municipalities in place of creating jobs. Where the community might not be able to use the product, then it could be sold by the manufacturer and the revenues donated to the community.

It might be reasonable to ask that any product being produced by automated labor would have a ratio of free giveaways to sales, following the innovative business models of firms like Toms Shoes, where for each pair of shoes sold, a free pair is provided to people in underprivileged communities. I believe that under this scenario companies could become very creative and proactive in coming up with ways to give back, including strategies to supplement UBI, if they wish to take full advantage of automation.

- *How do we start to prepare society for a future where the outlook for jobs is so uncertain?*
- *How can we mobilize individuals to take greater responsibility for their continual learning and future job opportunities?*
- *How can we test and debate radical new ideas around Universal Basic Incomes, automation taxes, and community profit sharing?*

A version of this chapter was originally published in FMCG News under the title "Is Automation Destined to Rewrite All Our Futures?"

Will Real-Life Blade Runners be Tax Collectors?

Rohit Talwar, Steve Wells, and Alexandra Whittington

Are robo-taxes an inevitable by-product of the replacement of humans by machines and will the robots be doing the collection?

Robots and Society

In 1979, an innovative two-minute TV commercial gave Britain a glimpse of the future. Choreographed to music from Rossini's Barber of Seville, hi-tech machines built the Fiat Strada. The tagline was "Handbuilt by Robots." Humans were nowhere to be seen in the Turin factory where the ad was shot, but the film crew knew where the people were: outside, on picket lines protesting the loss of their jobs.

The Robots are Coming

Fast forward nearly 40 years and "the robots are coming, they want to replace us, and there's nothing we can do to stop them" isn't the plot of the next season of Westworld, it's a real-world warning that's becoming louder with each new leap in the fields of artificial intelligence (AI) and robotics.

Both the technoprogressive enthusiasts and the head-in-the-sand reactionaries believe doomsayers are overstating the threat. After all, we don't all make cars. That is true, some of us dig ditches, some of us lay bricks, some of us milk cows. And there are now robots doing those jobs. But what if you take orders at a fast food outlet? McDonalds is replacing you with automation. Perhaps you're a lorry driver. Volvo, Uber, and others have already trialed driverless trucks—not always successfully. Indeed, what if you are a doctor, lawyer, accountant, architect, sales person, marketeer, pharmaceutical researcher, insurance claims analyst, building inspector, or engineer—all of whom are seeing AI, robots, and drones taking on part or all of roles traditionally performed by humans?

It's not even the case that a unique robot solution is required for each task; one model of robot produced by Kawasaki Heavy Industries of Japan can be adapted for use by a variety of businesses, including electronics manufacturers and drug companies. Furthermore, the latest Sawyer robot costs just US$19,000 and can teach itself tasks through observation without human intervention.

Can We Rely on History to Help Us Predict the Future?

On the one hand, some argue that economies have always adapted to the introduction of new technologies. In the early 1800s, looms were smashed by cotton and woolen workers who feared for their jobs, but in the end, to meet increased demand, more machines were needed and that meant more people to tend them. Employment levels remained about the same, it was just the nature of the work that changed. And we got used to horses being replaced by tractors, didn't we?

However, the counterargument is that the machines being brought in now are, or soon will be, smart enough to not need human supervision. The industries of the future could require far fewer, more highly skilled workers—this time we're becoming the horses.

The Luddites couldn't prevent the introduction of 19th century cutting-edge technology, the Turin car workers couldn't halt progress in the 1970s, and no amount of 21st century Canute-channeling can push back the current waves of change. Jobs are going to go: in the UK, a third by 2030 say some experts. In less than a decade and a half we could be looking at large-scale long-term unemployment. Fewer people working means less income tax, which means a government revenue shortfall, higher unemployment costs, and difficulties maintaining public service provision. This also means less citizen spending power to buy the goods and services being produced by the machines. The societal consequences could be devastating.

What Can We Do?

Many leaning to the right of British politics are pinning their hopes on business growth and employment being driven by the encouragement of free markets and lower corporate tax rates. They are trusting that unemployment costs will be met through revenues from corporate and individual taxes coupled with higher VAT takings.

Others advocate a more novel approach. Tax the robots.

But surely, we shouldn't tax innovation? That was the response of the EU's Digital Single Market Commissioner, Andrus Ansip, when Bill Gates suggested there should be a form of taxation on firms that use robots to take human jobs. Despite that reaction, Gates's idea is gaining traction: in the UK, Labour leader Jeremy Corbyn recently championed taxing advanced technology; in the USA, San Francisco now has a committee looking at how that might be done; and South Korea is leading the way by reducing tax incentives for investments in automation—not quite a robot tax, but close to it.

The thrust of the tax-the-robots notion is that robots and AI should be considered something that creates value for the owner, and companies cutting workforces are likely to be making higher profits. This represents a fundamental shift in the core notion that we should all seek employment to feed ourselves and families. Indeed, we could be seeing the shift to a different economic model—one whose ideal shape we don't yet know. Hence, the idea of applying additional taxation to companies that replace workers with robots or smart AIs to offset the loss of income tax caused by making humans redundant. In the long term, the economy may look so different that such conversations might be irrelevant, but for now we need a solution to what some see as a looming social and economic crisis—and robot taxes are the main option for debate right now.

Clearly, there's more to robot tax than merely balancing the Exchequer's books. Advocates of a robot tax want this money to be used to fund the foundations of the next economy; channeling the proceeds into adult retraining, education transformation, R&D, and unemployment provisions. A robot tax could pay for a fresh approach to education, one which develops the whole person, not just the future worker. This new approach would include life skills (cooking, health, and household management), interpersonal skills (listening, leadership, writing, and collaboration), and self-awareness (mindfulness, meditation, and mental health strategies). The underlying principle is that the value of automation should be used to benefit all of society, help us cross the "messy middle" transition period to a new economic model, and help to mitigate against future problems.

A Political Decision or the Right Decision?

Right now, we don't know how robot taxes would work in practice and the concept has become highly politicized.

One good starting point would be to (ironically) run powerful computer simulations of different scenarios for the pace of automation and the impacts on employment. These could be used as input to the development of economic models to explore the funding requirements of different public service strategies and how they might be met.

A next step might be to take a fresh look at taxation in general and cast an eye over options for adapting to a very different future. Several nations, including Finland and Germany—who are thought to be most likely to be among the first to implement some form of automation taxation mechanism—have already experimented with different forms of guaranteed or universal basic income. Such innovations may have an important part to play in how we deal with increased use of robots and AI.

While there are many supporters of the idea, taxing robots and AI will be hugely controversial; even agreeing the definition of robot and AI is likely to be an early stumbling block. Those wanting to encourage debate feel they are often deliberately misrepresented as the new anti-innovation Luddites—even though the ideas are supported by many at the frontiers of AI development. The advocates' view is that we should be taxing the proceeds of innovation to fund the new social and economic models being enabled by AI and its human liberating sister technologies such as robotics, cloud computing, hyperconnectivity, 3D/4D printing, synthetic biology, and nanotechnology. In response, there are already many unashamed proponents of low taxes, free markets, and wealth maximization using phrases such as unbridled socialism, communism, or Marxism to describe robot tax thinking. But, at present, no viable alternatives are being put on the table—and hope is not a very good strategy when planning the future for 7-9 billion people.

Of course, it may be that taxing robots turns out to be a temporary measure, as automation-heavy companies find their profits dwindling following the potential Rise of the Artisan, brought about by huge demand for products "hand-built by people."

- *What actions should individuals, companies, and governments be taking today to prepare for large-scale job displacement by automation?*
- *What could a world without work look like—how can we prepare ourselves for the transition?*
- *How might people's lives and purpose change if work was no longer a critical part of their existence?*

A version of this chapter was originally published in IT Pro Portal.

Key Uncertainties About the Future of Women

Rohit Talwar, Steve Wells, Alexandra Whittington, Helena Calle, and April Koury

How can business and society ensure a more positive future for women?

Rethinking the Future of Women

In the recent past, the issue of ensuring a truly equal future for women in society has risen up the agenda of global challenges—while at the same time indicators suggest the actual equality gap is growing globally on many indicators. From harassment and #metoo to #timesup and the rights to equal pay and equal access in education, the workplace, and the boardroom, women have been succeeding in spotlighting the issues and arguing for their rights. So, as we look to the future, some fundamental questions arise: What are the many possible futures of women? Are women's futures different from men's futures? How do we proceed in the coming years to embed a gender equality mindset while accounting for the unique challenges women face?

This chapter explores how business and society can adjust to ensure a more positive future for women, focusing on what we consider to be critical agenda issues. We conclude with our advice and dreams for the future of women.

Which Areas Could Benefit Significantly from the Increased Participation of Women?

As we look to the forces shaping our world, it is clear that society as a whole could benefit significantly from the increased participation of women in literally every domain, and in particular in the future of technology development, elected governmental roles, and higher education. For example, the 2018 book *Algorithms of oppression: How search engines reinforce racism* by Dr. Safiya Umoja Noble, highlights the kind of critical thinking the technology sector needs to be embracing about its broader social implications. The technology sector and governments need to better understand that an algorithm can be racist or sexist before rushing to integrate artificial intelligence (AI) into our social systems and institutions.

An increased participation of women in technology development could contribute significantly to the creation of more female-oriented products. For example, Natural Cycles, created by a woman, is an effective contraceptive app that gives women a natural choice over family planning, without the hormonal side effects of the pill. Many other similarly clever and effective technological solutions could be developed with an increased participation of women in technology. If automated systems, including those powered by AI, are representations of those who created them, then maybe those systems need to represent the gender split we see in society. More women in fields such as programming machine learning could help to create a gender balance within our intelligent technologies.

The Evolving Role of Women in the Workplace

In some domains and countries, the evolving role of women in the workplace is engendering a more confident and empowering attitude. Women are taking control of their own workplace situations and actively tackling inequalities. A variety of studies suggest that women's confidence when asking for a raise or a promotion is growing year by year. Women are realizing that the first step to change starts from within and these small changes can have a major impact on their work environment.

The future, as currently envisaged by many, depicts a world where much of the work that goes into creating products and services will be automated. Hence, what we offer our customers and clients could become increasingly commoditized, so our new propositions will need to focus on something different. Being more human and focusing on the relationship between businesses and customers could become a critical differentiator. As a result, the focus might shift to building propositions on a foundation of competences and values that are typically thought of as feminine—such as collaboration, relationship development, and empathy. Such an approach could help firms create the differentiated and more sustainable competitive advantage they need in the future. The role of women across business could become increasingly crucial here in leading the culture change required to underpin the development of new propositions.

Significant Challenges Facing Women Professionals in the Years to Come

Many women professionals face the continuing challenge of leading a household and maintaining a career. Societal pressure to "have it all," however, may be taking a new shape. Evidence suggests that women from the millennial generation across the globe have not married or had children at the same levels as their predecessors. Hence, a woman's versatile balancing act across various personal and professional roles in the future may not necessarily be due to motherhood, but rather, a choice made for personal fulfillment.

Women professionals face the challenge of establishing a new relationship with the men in their lives. Men, as working colleagues or as relationship partners, are used to the stereotypical idea of providing higher economic support and assuming leadership roles. The challenge now is to create new ways of relating to each other based on an authentic mutual partnership.

Cultural norms vary significantly across the world, but evidence on the rise of women in business and being more prominent in society is clear in Asia, for example. And yet, even in the developed world, we still see institutional discrimination. The cultural and deep-rooted context for discrimination is likely to take some time to clear and is only likely to change through a combination of active campaigning, legislative change, behavioral modification, and generational trends.

Will the Man-Woman Divide Persist in the Next Decade?

The gap is a big one. In November 2017, the World Economic Forum (WEF) estimated that, at current rates, it will take 217 years to close the gap on pay and employment opportunities. Sadly, this estimate has risen by 47 years over the figure calculated a year earlier. Perhaps nations should look to follow Iceland's fair pay example and eliminate the idea that women and men at work deserve different treatment in the first place. The WEF also estimate that the broader gender gap—that takes account of factors such as healthcare, education, and participation in politics—has risen from 83 to 100 years over the same one-year period.

If we define "the man-woman divide" as sexual dimorphism, for example that our differences extend beyond just our physical organs, then certainly it seems likely that this will continue. The man-woman divide will probably persist, although there is some concern that male fertility in the West could be threatened by hormonal disruptions in the food chain and our natural ecosystems. However, the roles of each of the genders might become more similar. There could be less men- or women-oriented services, products, or roles. This might be the beginning of the next era where, in 20 years from now, the man-woman divide could become much less perceptible.

As with many norms that become unacceptable as our collective sense of right and wrong evolves, from one perspective, a gradual erosion of alpha male domination looks set to take place. Through the empowerment of women, supported by the increasing enlightenment among men, societies could start to accelerate the agenda for equality. This will be aided by the power of technologies such as social media as platforms for campaigning and "outing unacceptable practices." At another level, the dominance of strong male leaders of major economies such as Donald Trump, Xi Jinping, and Vladimir Putin, suggests that traditional male hierarchies may be hard to dislodge.

Women's Ability to Manage Risks and Challenges

Is society responsible for preparing women for the risks and challenges of the future? How should we help them respond to economic shocks, the failure of social institutions, and the challenge of adapting to the automation of work—potentially displacing many jobs? Perhaps the best way to do this is to increase the participation in and completion of post-secondary education by women worldwide.

It has been thought that men are more prone to taking risks and overcoming challenges than women. Psychological research has debunked this myth and now we know that these differences depend of the type of risky behaviors we include in the research questionnaires. It is not that one gender is more prone to risk taking than the other. Rather, we are all capable of developing these capacities depending on the experiences we have had and the situations we face.

Are there innate abilities that women have that can be nurtured through education, in work training, and coaching? Could this help raise women's awareness of their own capabilities, while also allowing them to demonstrate competence in managing risks and challenges in leadership positions?

Advice to Women on Tackling the Future

In a world increasingly dominated by the hype and reality of technology, women need to adjust their expectations of this growing force in society. Even though we encounter abundant conventional wisdom that says humans will be replaced by technology, this is a line pushed by the technoprogressives with a vested interest, and women in particular shouldn't fall for it. The future, especially one highly imbued with AI, needs humanity, and especially women, more than ever.

The future is waiting for women to take on any leadership role where they feel they can contribute to society. The world as we know it is changing, and now is the time to evolve a new generation with higher expectations of what women can do. The critical challenge here is for women to believe in themselves and encourage other women to do so as well.

The key here is for women to focus on maximizing their potential as women. This means celebrating their natural skills and sense of the importance of relationships, empathy, collaboration, and caring. Ultimately these are the traits that could make the difference between a dystopian technology-enabled world and a very human future.

Achievements in the Progress of Women We Hope to be Talking About in Five Years' Time

In five years, we hope to see better legislation worldwide to protect women's health and access to education. Hopefully more countries will adopt gender-blind wage policies like Iceland. Also, we hope to see greater priority placed on bringing maternal and infant mortality rates down to near zero globally within five years, using strategies that empower women and make best use of local knowledge.

In five years, we truly hope that we will finally have zero tolerance of female genital mutilation everywhere. We hope that all women in the world have full access to education. And that women participate in at least half of the leadership roles in the corporate and political sectors.

Across the next set of electoral cycles, it would be a pleasant surprise if half of all the developed world's major democracies were led by a woman and if the supporting legislatures were gender balanced.

- *What are the hurdles that women face in reaching their potential in your organization?*
- *What can we do to ensure that enlightened views on the role of women in society can penetrate the traditional and cultural norms that exist in some countries?*
- *How might more women in senior roles in politics and business change how society responds to challenges and opportunities?*

A version of this chapter was originally published in Fresh Business Thinking under the title "The Future for Women—Where Will We Be in Five Years?"

Fembots vs. HAL—Gender, Bias, and the People of AI

Rohit Talwar, Steve Wells, Alexandra Whittington, and Helena Calle

From Watson to Sophia, who are the artificially intelligent robot personas of today, and what can they tell us about the future of gendered technology?

Gendered Technology–Humanizing or Stereotyping?

The potential loss of our humanity to soulless machines is one of the biggest concerns around the exponentially advancing technologies that are entering every aspect of human activity. The technology sector has tried to sweeten the pill with attempts to humanize the applications, chatbots, and devices they want us to embed into our daily lives. The issue here is that we may be seeing the replication of gender stereotypes and unconscious biases in the design of these systems, which could have massively damaging consequences for society if the process continues unchecked. A review of the current range of developments reveals the scale of the challenge ahead.

Siri. Alexa. Cortana. These familiar names are the modern-day Girl Fridays making everyone's life easier. These virtual assistants powered by artificial intelligence (AI) bring to life the digital tools of the information age. One of the subtle strategies designers use to make it easier for us to integrate AI into our lives is "anthropomorphism"— the attribution of human-like traits to non-human objects. However, the rise of AI with distinct personalities, voices, and physical forms is not as benign as it might seem. As futurists who are interested in the impacts of technology on society, we wonder what role human-like technologies play in achieving human-centered futures.

For example, do anthropomorphized machines enable a future wherein humanity can thrive? Or, do human-like AIs foreshadow a darker prognosis, particularly in relation to gender roles and work? This chapter looks at a continuum of human-like personas that give a face to AI technology. As you read the examples below, we ask you to consider two questions: What could it mean for our collective future if technology is increasingly human-like and gendered? And, what does it tell us about our capacity to create a very equal, inclusive, and gender-balanced human future?

The Women of AI

One of the most important observations we want to convey is that the typical consumer-facing AI persona is highly feminine and feminized. There are several robots and AIs that take a female form. The examples below show the sheer breadth of applications where a feminine persona and voice are deliberately used to help us feel comfortable with increasingly invasive technology:

- *Emma:* Brain Corp's autonomous floor cleaner Emma (Enabling Mobile Machine Automation) is no chatty fembot. She is designed to clean large spaces like schools and hospitals. Currently, Emma is being piloted at various Wal-Mart locations, where the human cleaning crew is being asked to embrace a robot-supporting role—even though it may ultimately replace some of them. Emma washes floors independently using a combination of AI, the lidar light-based remote sensing method, and smart sensors.
- *Alexa:* Amazon's Alexa is the disembodied feminine AI that lives inside a smart device. As a personal assistant, Alexa does it all. There are versions of Alexa for hotels, some that act as your DJ, and those that provide medical advice. There is another side to Alexa, however; one that secretly records your private conversations. This

is a great example of how companion AIs embody the surveillance of Big Brother with the compassion of Big Mother rolled into one.

- *Siri:* Like Alexa, Apple's Siri is an AI-powered woman's voice. The iPhone assistant is helpful and direct. You can find information, get where you need to go, and organize your schedule. Lately, Siri is attempting to learn jokes and develop more of a natural rapport with users. Can brushing up on social skills help virtual assistant AIs shed their reputation for being both nosy and dull?

- *Cara:* In the legal industry, Casetext's Cara (Case Analysis Research Assistant) is an algorithmic legal assistant that uses machine learning to conduct research. Cara is widely available to attorneys and judges, a great example of AI replacing professional jobs with a powerfully smart feminine figure. With Cara, we have to wonder if there are too many outdated assumptions about gender involved—why is Cara a legal assistant, and not an attorney like Ross, the world's first robot lawyer?

- *Kate:* This specialized travel robot from SITA is an AI mobile passenger check-in kiosk. Kate uses big data related to airport passenger flows to move autonomously about the airport, going where she is most needed to reduce lines and wait times. Kate, like many AI programs, uses big data predictively, perhaps displaying something similar to women's intuition.

- *Sophia:* This humanoid robot from Hanson Robotics gained notoriety as the first robot to claim a form of citizenship. Debuted in 2017, Sophia is a recognized citizen of the nation of Saudi Arabia, and the first robot with legal personhood. Sophia can carry on conversations and answer interesting questions. But with her quirky personality and exaggerated female features, some might categorize Sophia as a great example of AI as hype over substance.

- *Ava:* As one of the newest female AIs, Autodesk's Ava seems to take extreme feminization a step further. A "digital human," Ava is a beautiful and helpful AI chatbot avatar that can read people's body language. Ava is programmed to be emotionally expressive. Her customer service job is to support engineering and architectural software product users in real time. Being able to detect emotions puts Ava in an entirely new league of female virtual assistants. So do her looks: Ava's appearance is literally based on a stunning actress from New Zealand.

The Men of AI

What about the male personas? Probably the most well-known AI is Watson, the IBM machine that's matched its immense wits against human opponents at chess and the trivia gameshow Jeopardy. Watson has also been used in cancer diagnosis and has a regular role in many more industries, including transportation, financial services, and education. When it comes to the masculine, it seems both brain and brawn are required. In many cases, male robots do the literal heavy lifting. Here are some examples of the jobs male-personified AIs currently do:

- *Botler:* A chatbot called Botler seems enlightened. He provides legal information and services for immigrants and victims of sexual harassment. Botler wears a smile and tuxedo with bowtie, appearing to be a helpful proto-butler-like gentleman.
- *Stan:* Stanley Robotics' robotic valet Stan parks your car. An autonomous forklift, Stan is able to strategically fill parking garages to capacity. Does Stan reinforce gender-based stereotypes about cars and driving?
- *FRAnky:* At Frankfurt Airport you can meet FRAnky, a Facebook Messenger-based chatbot that can search for flights and give information about restaurants, shops, and the airport Wi-Fi service.
- *Leo:* Another travel pro, SITA's Leo is a luggage-drop robot who prints a bag tag, checks your suitcase, then prints a baggage receipt. The curbside helper is strong and smart.
- *Ross:* The world's first robo-lawyer. The phenomenal computational power Ross uses for legal research saves attorneys time, effort, and mistakes. The proliferation of data is the main rationale for the rise of the robo-lawyer. Human attorneys are expensive and time-consuming when it comes to the drudge work

of digging up information; proponents of Ross say the AI saves 20-30 hours research time per case.

- *DaVinci:* Intuitive Surgical's DaVinci surgical assistant is one of the most established names in the robotics field. Named after the artist Leonardo DaVinci, this robot is reported to be cutting hospital stay times, improving patient outcomes, and reducing medical mistakes. Like Ross, DaVinci suggests a future where even highly skilled professional roles could be at risk from robots, which could impact the large proportion of men in these jobs.

Technology's Transformative Potential

These examples raise the question of how much does technology shape reality. The personal computer and the mobile phone, for instance, have had immeasurable impacts across society and changed everything from work and healthcare to politics and education. Think about all the things that didn't exist before the rise of the iPhone: texting and driving, selfies, online dating, Uber and Twitter, these are just some of the new normal. The way we work, live, and play have all been transformed by the rise of the information age. Hence, as we scan the next horizon, there is a strong sense that AI will form the basis of the near-future evolution of society.

Overall, we find it interesting to ponder the human-like manifestations among AI companions. A close look at the people of AI raises many questions: What is the role of human intelligence in an AI world? What will the relationship between robots and people be like in the workplace and in the home? How might humanity be redefined as more AI computers gain citizenship, emotional intelligence, and possibly even legal rights? How can we avoid reinforcing unhealthy gender stereotypes through technology?

We don't expect to get straight to the answers. Rather, we use these questions to start meaningful conversations about how to construct a very human future.

- *What are the possible societal implications of AI personas reinforcing gender stereotypes?*
- *What are the characteristics of the AI incarnations you choose to interact with or avoid?*
- *Can organizations embrace the technology and at the same time question the underlying gender-based design assumptions in off-the-shelf AI tools?*

A version of this chapter was originally published in Relocate Global under the title "Is AI Following Gender Stereotypes?"

Disrespectful Tech—Ten Ways Artificial Intelligence Could Transform Your Finances and Your Life

Rohit Talwar, Steve Wells, Alexandra Whittington, April Koury, and Maria Romero

Would you trust a robot with your money?

The Potential Impact of AI on Personal Banking

After President Trump and Brexit, artificial intelligence (AI) is perhaps the hottest topic of debate around the world. There are many ways in which this most disrespectful technology could change how we might save, spend, and invest in the future. To help understand its life-changing potential, here are ten ways we have identified for how AI might impact and enhance our experience of personal banking:

1. *Enhanced Security and Fraud Protection*—By monitoring every transaction as it happens and comparing it to historical patterns, AI could identify fraud in progress, such as the customer's personal bank account being drained. Equally it can detect warning signs; the customer's financial advisor being

unavailable, changing their spending habits, and buying one-way flights to the Bahamas, for example.

2. *Go Compare on Steroids*–Artificial intelligence could take the concept of price comparison websites to new heights. Collating different legally accessible savings and loan options from across all providers around the world, an AI finance supermarket tool could instantly identify financial products that meet the client's requirements precisely, highlighting pertinent small print, and exposing hidden costs. Through an ongoing subscription, this continuous comparison tool could make recommendations to the customer or be authorized to switch financial products automatically as better options emerge.

3. *Spending Comparison and Budgeting*–AI would allow us to compare the spending of individuals, households, and businesses. Various views could be available, for example how much do we spend on electricity, food, stationery, or transport relative to people with similar incomes, households of the same size, or comparable businesses to ours.

4. *Aggregated Purchasing*–A bank could aggregate customer purchase information on an opt-in basis and use it to secure higher discounts from providers based on the total spending power of its customer base. Deals could be offered by vendors, with customers' personal AI assistants deciding whether to buy based on learned needs and interests—only consulting with us when the AI doesn't know enough to make a choice.

5. *Dynamic Fund Management*–The AI systems could look at estimated future spending based on past behavior and move bank customers' spare cash into whichever savings or investment products offered the best return based on the level of risk the client was prepared to take. Options might range from a stable interest-bearing account to highly volatile digital currency funds.

6. *Digital Currency Trading*–With growing investor interest in digital currencies like Bitcoin, Litecoin, and Ether, banks could trade the funds clients allocate to this asset class—buying and

selling on a dynamic basis as currency values fluctuate or tracking the choices of the best cryptotraders.

7. *Financial Equality*–While individuals with limited funds may not be able to pay for a human financial advisor, AI may become the great financial equalizer. Constantly declining technology prices would enable literally everyone to access the best AI investment advice at almost no cost.

8. *Dynamic Pricing*–Based on past behavior data, AI could predict what price each individual would consider fair. Prices would be public, but each individual would only see those customized just for them.

9. *The "Jiminy Cricket" of Personal Budgeting*–Smart systems would nudge us to make the best decisions for our financial situation. For example, for most 20-somethings, instead of spending a month's salary on Friday night, it would encourage more modest entertainment options and invest the rest to help achieve our holiday or retirement goals. The AI might go a stage further and add a small auto-saving amount to each purchase— automatically squirreling the funds away at each purchase.

10. *My Digital Banking Twin*–Our personal AI clones or "digital twins" would be authorized to buy, save, sell, or trade on our account. Credit card purchases, bank transactions, bill payments, completing student loan or mortgage applications, and even impulse buys could all be delegated to our digital twin. These transactions would be conducted under the watchful eye of the bank's own AI Big Brother to make sure a digital twin doesn't go rogue, get hacked, or collude with another to defraud their human counterparts.

Personal Finance Reshaped

The applications of AI are nigh on limitless and we can expect to see them proliferate in the marketplace over the next few years. Some may thrive, others may be absorbed by larger institutions, the majority will end up as a failure statistic like most technology start-ups of the past, but the ideas will live on in a constantly transforming personal finance landscape. The fun part is trying to pick the winners and convincing our own providers to up their game and bring a little AI spice into our financial lives.

- *Where would you most like to see AI being used in the management of your finances?*
- *Which are the financial situations where you'd still require a human touch?*
- *What are the biggest benefits and risks that you can foresee from greater use of AI in managing your finances?*

A version of this chapter was originally published in The Money Pages under the title "Would You Trust a Robot with Your Money?"

The Big Reboot, Part 1 —Rethinking Education and Employment in an Automated Era

Rohit Talwar, Steve Wells, Alexandra Whittington, Helena Calle, and April Koury

In the face of widespread and accelerating automation, how can we reskill society and create new job opportunities?

Creating Businesses and Employment in a Turbulent Economy

The Big Reboot is a two-part exploration of how we prepare society for the potential impacts of technological disruption, job automation, and the continuing shifts taking place in the global economy. In this first discussion we look at practical strategies for i) raising skills and digital literacy across society, and ii) generating the new ventures and job openings required to fill the employment gap left by those that are displaced by technology.

We are reaching peak hysteria in the debate about the potential impact of artificial intelligence (AI) and automation on tasks, roles, jobs, employment, and incomes. On an almost weekly basis, we see projections of wholesale job devastation through automation. These doom-laden forecasts vie with outlandishly optimistic forecasts from AI vendors and consultants suggesting that millions of new roles will be created because of our smart new tech toys. In practice, we are simply too early in its evolution to have any sense of the likely outcomes of this Fourth Industrial Revolution—the latest wave of change driven by exponentially advancing technologies.

Automation and the Economy—Five Key Uncertainties
Right now, the world is legitimately clueless about five key factors:

1. *How far and how deep will these technologies actually penetrate over the next five to twenty years?*
2. *What level of opportunities could be generated in the new sectors and businesses that might emerge?*
3. *How might the nature of work, roles, jobs, and workplaces evolve over time?*
4. *How might governments, businesses, and individuals respond and what is the potential for innovative job generation solutions to emerge?*
5. *What might the net impact of these accelerating waves of technological change be on employment and the economic prospects for the individual?*

So, getting beyond the debate and the hype, as futurists we believe we should be redirecting our energies across government, business, and society, challenging old assumptions and limiting paradigms to conduct previously unthinkable experiments to help us prepare for the next two decades. Hence, our focus is on designing and testing solutions for a range of possible "next futures" and for the scenarios of what might follow them. Why? In our view, it seems naive and dangerous to rely on the alternative strategy of simply betting on the hope that growth and innovation will save us.

Thinking the Unthinkable

We argue that now is the time to be thinking the unthinkable about: 1) preparing the workforce for an uncertain future; 2) creating new jobs and businesses; 3) providing for the unemployed in a fair, dignified, and straightforward manner that supports their search for opportunities; and 4) funding the transitions from today's economy to future ones. To help stimulate action, with this chapter we build on some of the concepts presented in our recent books *Beyond Genuine Stupidity—Ensuring AI Serves Humanity* and *The Future Reinvented—Reimagining Life, Society, and Business* to present a range of experimental ideas in the first two of those domains—education and job creation.

We caveat these ideas with the acknowledgment that they too might only be temporary solutions in a fast-changing world. Some believe that we might be seeing the beginning of the end of jobs as the primary means of feeding our families and that, within 20 years, AI may have transformed the notions of work and employment as we know them. Others are suggesting that the economy will be reinvented by exponential technologies such as AI, 3D/4D printing, synthetic biology, lab grown food, vertical farming, autonomous vehicles, hyperloop transport, and smart materials. The belief is that these technologies are creating a level of societal abundance that eliminates the need to work and breaks the link between our physical earnings and our access to goods and services. All this may be true and will be the subject of future explorations. For now, we want to focus on the next 10-20 years and a world where work, employment, and incomes are still likely to be central tenets of economic management. So, what are some of the core experiments we could be pursuing in the fields of adult education and job creation?

Educating Society

What's becoming abundantly clear is that at the national, business, and individual level, what will determine our ability to survive and thrive in a rapidly evolving landscape are our levels of education and big picture awareness. Our capacity to navigate a turbulent landscape will be driven by a number of factors: 1) our understanding of how the world is changing; 2) our capacity to think, reason, and solve problems; 3) our ability to learn new skills and approaches quickly; 4) our mastery of life skills such as collaboration, scenario thinking, coping with uncertainty, and handling complexity; and 5) our digital literacy. On the latter, countries like Finland are leading the way with their innovative free online offering designed to teach the entire nation about AI.

Collectively, these skills will help us move from role to role in a world where job tenures are shortening but lifespans could be increasing. They will also help us start our own businesses and take greater responsibility for our own livelihoods. This is something that could become an increasing priority as medium to large organizations slim down their workforces through competitive pressures and automation. We can see a growing onus on small to medium enterprises to provide the bulk of employment across the economy. Hence, some of the key policy experiments we are advocating are outlined below.

Future Immersion Intensives—It is now common for business executives to attend immersive study tours to meet new ventures in emerging sectors or take part in transformative one- to two-week courses at institutions like Singularity University. These are designed to accelerate "mindset change" in these organizations by providing a crash course in the ideas shaping the future and the technologies that might deliver them. A similar, lower cost, society wide option would be to create a range of such programs ranging in length from a weekend to a month. They would combine business visits, lectures, projects, and discussions with innovators, change agents, and entrepreneurs. The programs would be aimed at those in work, the unemployed, students, parents, teachers, and those who realize their business has to change. The faculty could be drawn from business, academia, and those in the local community who are retired or unemployed but have a desire to serve and grow at the same time.

Acknowledging the Shift to a Graduate Level Workforce—Automation seems highly likely to reduce the number of lower and mid-level skilled jobs in the economy. We can see a scenario where, within five to ten years, 80% of the new jobs created will require a graduate level education or equivalent. This means a cornerstone of any employment policy has to be to ensure we are readjusting the skills and knowledge base in the country at every level. In particular, this means encouraging and incentivizing adults to enter into continuing education while still in employment. Equally it means confidence building programs for the unemployed, basic literacy support for those who have been left behind, and a massive expansion of access schemes to allow those with few or no formal qualifications to transition into higher education.

Expanding Access—Funding will always be an issue—but the cost of inaction and a poorly educated workforce could far outweigh a large-scale expansion in provision. This could be delivered in innovative ways—including encouraging firms to sponsor local education programs either through direct funding, providing tutors, or allowing the use of their unused meeting and training room facilities during the day, in the evenings, and at weekends. Vacant facilities in schools, colleges, and universities could also be used in the same way.

A key part of the learning agenda here would be to take people into new and emerging businesses to help them understand the changing nature of work and workplaces and learn about the skills they require now and in the future. Support systems could be provided for communities to self-organize education and skills programs, sourcing tutors locally, and using attendee ratings and feedback to determine who best serves the needs of local communities. Clearly, pump priming might be required for areas where no such local tutoring talent exists. The key is to try a range of experiments, share the experiences, and scale the best practice models for different types and size of local community.

Abolishing Student Debt and Tuition Fees—In the UK, students are typically finishing higher education with debts of £30,000—£60,000 and, in many cases, poor job prospects and relatively low morale. This is the very group that needs to be inspired to create new ideas, services, and businesses for a changing world. Hence, a cancellation of student debt and individually paid tuition fees might help make it more attractive to go into higher education—especially if meaningful student grants were re-introduced.

Training and Education Salaries—For those who are made redundant or struggling to find work in their current sector, an option might be to retrain for a new career or sector. Here, a government funded salary could be payable for the duration of a training program or degree course.

Associations and Guilds with Training Salaries—To help deliver on the above retraining requirements, new salaried models of vocational training could be developed by evolving existing professional bodies and creating new ones. Their primary purpose would be to help develop the skills and personal competencies required for the new world of work. These programs would combine work-specific training, work placements, and the development of general work, business, and social skills. A training salary would be paid throughout the retraining period to take away the associated stress of taking time out to learn new skills.

Incentivizing Learning—Continuing professional development might have to become compulsory or be incentivized through the tax system to encourage individuals to keep acquiring skills to help them move from job to job.

Investment in Job Creation

Alongside reskilling the nation and changing mindsets, a parallel process is required to help stimulate new jobs, and to grow the businesses and industry sectors that will provide them. A number of potential experiments are described below.

Start-Up Salaries—Those starting new businesses could be offered a government top-up to ensure that employer and worker salaries are payable at a reasonable level for the first few years, enabling these firms to focus on their growth and development through a crucial period.

Investment in Future Sectors—The scale of competition between nations is intensifying and there is a clear belief that technologies like AI, blockchain, the Internet of Things, synthetic biology, and quantum computing will be the key battlegrounds. Hence, a major expansion in public funding for research and development across a range of domains is required to ensure the country is identifying and creating jobs in the key science, technology, and innovation sectors of the future. The scale of public investment will need to keep pace with global leaders to ensure the nation can compete in the future.

Laying the Foundations for the Future—The industries of the future are likely to be highly data intensive, global, and demanding of superfast broadband to help them stay connected and responsive in an always on world. To accelerate the attraction of these new sectors, governments will also need to ensure that they are delivering broadband infrastructures which match the best in the world.

New Models of Start-Up and Early Stage Venture Investment Funds—The new models would see government matching the investments made into these funds by individuals and business. Investment would be open to anyone globally who wanted to back start-ups through these funds, which would take a share in the equity of each business they invest in. Individual investments into the funds could range from £1 to £1 million with no special tax reliefs. To reduce administrative costs and speed up the process, the investments would be made using a standard model and contract structure, with high levels of technology support to manage the process and report to investors on the progress and needs of each business.

The investor community would help do the due diligence on the potential investments, and those investment opportunities with the greatest employment potential would be prioritized. A condition of receiving money is that the investee business would invest a proportion of future profits in such funds every year. Any profits received from the investee businesses and from the sale of such companies would be rolled up into the fund for the first few years until the funds are established as robust.

The administrative staff running the fund could be resourced using venture capital fund secondees provided as part of their firm's corporate responsibility endeavors. The more junior staff could be provided by consultancy, legal, and accounting firms looking to provide innovative training experiences for their younger employees.

Compulsory Corporate Investment Funds–For a fixed period of time, while the economy is in transition, every business could be mandated to invest a fixed proportion of profits to help with start-up creation via the funds described above.

Investing Corporate Cash Surpluses–For those holding large cash surpluses, a similar approach would be to mandate those companies to invest a proportion of that cash into national investment funds. These would again back new ventures, early stages firms, and, in particular, more established businesses looking to grow. This could accelerate job creation on a massive scale and put corporate surpluses to use in the economy.

Total Employment Responsibility–Under this model, each firm would be responsible for ensuring a certain level of employment in the economy, calculated by AI systems based on the previous year's revenue as a proportion of total private sector turnover. This might be delivered through direct employment, subcontractors, and suppliers who work solely for you, or the creation of jobs in new businesses which you support.

Employers' Collectives–Firms could pool their total employment responsibility commitments into collectives—paying a fee per job to be created. The collectives would effectively take on the responsibility of starting and supporting start-ups, and providing grants, loans, and equity.

Deferred Redundancy—In this model, workers made redundant would remain on a firm's payroll at full pay until they find a new job. This would incentivize firms to provide training and job finding support to those who they make redundant.

Public Service Expansion—Across the world, most public services such as education, healthcare, transport, environment management, and emergency services are struggling to meet their own responsibilities and public expectations. These services can all reasonably expect greater future service demand in a period of upheaval and transition. Improving the quality of public services could help raise morale across society. The focus of these new jobs could be targeted on public-facing activities. Staff would be on fixed term contracts with strong continuous learning opportunities that encourage the individuals to acquire higher-level capabilities and move on into the private sector.

Investment in the Arts and Social Sciences—In a world where technology could play a much bigger role in traditionally supported professions, we need to think laterally about where human roles will still be prevalent. The performing and creative arts are likely to remain sectors where we will want to see humans in action rather than robots. Equally, the social sciences require strong analytical and intuitive capabilities which are currently beyond the scope of AI. Furthermore, the addition of unique human perspectives is often what makes social science insights more profound and compelling. Hence, both these sectors could be key job creators if we can fund their expansion and the growth in the number of associated higher education places made available.

Embracing Experimentation

These are just a handful of the many ideas we have been exploring for how to address the challenges presented by a world in transition. There are no answers at present—only ideas that warrant investigation and experimentation to see how we can reskill society and create new job opportunities in a world where the individual is still expected to take responsibility for the wellbeing and shelter of their dependents.

The second part of this series will look at ideas for supporting the unemployed and will then go on to deal with the critical question of how all the various ideas and initiatives might be funded. For those who are particularly concerned about such issues and the impacts on debt and taxation, we would also ask them to consider what the cost of inaction might be. It is also worth bearing in mind that if a nation can pioneer innovative solutions in each of these areas, the results could be attractive to other nations—creating new service industry opportunities.

- *How do we persuade business leaders and politicians to debate the thinkable and the unthinkable openly?*
- *What support might business seek from government to create a localized job creation ecosystem?*
- *What approaches could be tested to help businesses engage in job creation?*

The Big Reboot, Part 2—The Economic Impacts of Societal Transitions

Rohit Talwar, Steve Wells, Alexandra Whittington, Helena Calle, and April Koury

How can we address a rise in the number of "technologically unemployed" and fund the costs of navigating a turbulent economic transition period?

People and Money

This is the second part of The Big Reboot—a two-part exploration of how we can rethink and experiment with the mechanisms that might help prepare society for technological disruption, automation, and continuing global economic shifts. Part one explored ideas for reskilling society and creating new job opportunities. In this chapter, we explore different ways of supporting the unemployed as they look to transition back into work and at mechanisms for funding all of the ideas explored across both chapters.

In The Big Reboot, Part 1—Rethinking Education and Employment in an Automated Era, we suggested that society cannot possibly know or predict the true impacts of technological disruption on the economy and workforce over the next 20 years. We also argued that our response should not be to sit and hope for innovation and growth to save us.

Instead, we believe that now is the time to be thinking the unthinkable, challenging old orthodoxies, and doing experiments that can provide the evidence on which future strategies can be based.

In particular, we want to stimulate new thinking about: 1) preparing the workforce for an uncertain future; 2) creating new jobs and businesses; 3) supporting the unemployed in a fair, dignified, and straightforward manner that enables their search for opportunities; and 4) funding the transitions from this economy to future ones. To help stimulate action, the two chapters build on some of the concepts presented in our recent books *Beyond Genuine Stupidity—Ensuring AI Serves Humanity* and *The Future Reinvented—Reimagining Life, Society, and Business* to present a range of experimental ideas. Here we focus on the latter two domains—supporting the unemployed and funding the transition.

Rethinking Unemployment

Even before the potential crisis of persistent technological unemployment is upon us, the battle lines have been drawn between those for and against ideas like Universal Basic Incomes (UBI). We would argue that the debate should be informed by a wide range of policy experiments that reflect views across the entire spectrum of opinions. The key seems to be ensuring that unemployment is not stigmatized. Rather, it should instead be treated as a period where the individual is rebuilding their confidence, acquiring news skills, developing a new business, or serving the community. The discussion and experimentation can then shift to exploring how best to support them to feel like a valued member of society. To that end, here are some of the ideas we have been exploring.

Guaranteed Basics

Universal/Guaranteed Basic Incomes—There will inevitably be employment casualties from the process of automation. The question arises as to the extent to which people will be able to afford the goods and services now being produced by the machines if they no longer have jobs. Many are arguing for provision of a guaranteed UBI across society—that pays a living wage to everyone—at a rate typically higher than unemployment benefit. Countries around the world from Canada and Finland to India and Namibia have been experimenting with different models for how this might work. At the time of writing, the newly elected coalition government of Italy has a manifesto commitment to introduce such a mechanism.

The risk of rising long-term unemployment is a real one, and something will need to be done. Simply ignoring the reality and insisting that people find work won't solve the problem or feed their dependents. We believe governments could work together to conduct a range of UBI experiments. The aim would be to test different delivery models and payment levels to see the impacts on take-up, funding costs, economic activity, the shadow economy, social wellbeing, crime, domestic violence, and mental health. There are already strongly polarized political views on such an option. However, doing the experiments is not committing to the policy, but will provide evidence on which to base policy decisions when the need for action arises.

Conditional Basic Incomes—One of the arguments against UBI is that a large proportion of the population simply don't need or want it and that the money would make little difference to them. To address this, a conditional scheme would make payments available to those below a certain income level as a top-up to get them to a guaranteed earnings level. This could replace a lot of unemployment and work-related benefits, be available to all to apply, and administered in a fairer more transparent way with AI ensuring equitable treatment for all.

Community Service UBI—Under this model, the receipt of UBI would be tied to the individual undertaking some form of community service reinvestment. With public sector budgets being cut in many places and declining provision of services such as libraries, health visitors, and maintenance of public spaces, UBI could be delivered in the form of community grants meant to counter austerity measures. In return for the receipt of UBI, individuals would choose service projects (community gardens, walking trails, artwork, etc.) that would deliver a public benefit, give the individual a sense of purpose and achievement, create new connections, and enable the acquisition of new skills.

Such schemes could also be supported with technology that encourages local programs that promote socialization: clubs, groups, hobby networks, for example, that encourage people to get away from screens and spend time with their neighbors. Overall, this idea is about using UBI to build civic culture and counter the negative impacts of technology on communities. This may mean rethinking how technology is used to bring people together and making the most of it. Another approach would be for individuals to pool their UBI to start and run these programs themselves—which might help them qualify for additional funds and resources for their projects.

Guaranteed Basic Products—Some might call this a modern-day version of food stamps. Under this model, which might run alongside some form of UBI, all that were eligible would receive credits to be used on key products such as clothing and healthy foodstuff from a range of stores. Government might seek to use such a measure to tackle critical food-related health issues in society. So, for example, certain unhealthy products might be excluded selectively or universally on a health basis. Hence, diabetics might be completely excluded from purchasing anything adversely indicated for them.

Guaranteed Basic Services—Here, those who claim the option could receive services free at the point of consumption—from travel and all forms of healthcare through to water, electricity, and gas. Again, governments might use such measures to nudge desirable societal health and environmental behaviors—through free gym access and free public transport as an alternative to private vehicle ownership.

Funding the Transition

The experiments suggested here have not been costed as they could be applicable to nations across the globe and the experimental models adopted for similar ideas might vary dramatically. Our view is that doing nothing is not an option. The population needs to see governments facing up to radical shifts in society with investment in equally radical policy experiments. Here are a few examples of what could be done.

Robot Taxes—A lot of the potential issues around the introduction of AI and other disruptive technologies will arise from the choices made by employers. Will they retain the staff freed up by technology or release them in pursuit of cost saving and higher profits? While we cannot and do not want to hold back innovation, there is a need to explore how to fund the resulting social costs. One option being proposed is the use of so-called robot or automation taxes. Here firms would pay a higher rate of taxes on the profits they derive from increased automation. This has met with a lot of opposition from businesses and many economists but has some support from technology pioneers in Silicon Valley.

Tax Enforcement—A less radical option would be for governments to start using technologies such as AI to beef up enforcement and collect what they are rightly owed under the law. Globally, governments are struggling to fund their current commitments and many services are overstretched. There is also strong opposition to raising taxes to fund service improvement. However, this might not be required if people and companies simply paid what they are legally supposed to and didn't use avoidance mechanisms. For a fixed period of time, loopholes, avoidance opportunities, and so-called "negotiated sweetheart deals" would be abolished. Using AI, governments would systematically check every individual and business to ensure they were paying what they should do under the law and collect retrospective debts going back as far as the law would allow.

The New Tax Collectors—Rather than recruiting more tax inspectors, government could outsource collection to lawyers and accountants who would do the investigations on a "no win, no fee" basis—investigating those that are not their own clients. Having advised for years on how to avoid tax, they know where to look for the gold. They could be assigned lists of targets to go after and paid a proportion of the fees collected. Of course, they might also generate fees from advising their clients on how to deal with such investigations.

Taxation at the Point of Purchase—Large companies, particularly those in the technology arena, have often avoided paying taxes where the transactions are undertaken. Instead, they have issued invoices and reported their profits in a different lower tax location. Simple rule changes would require firms to pay the tax in the markets where the clients reside. Again, tax lawyers and accountants would be able to provide long lists of reasons why this is not such a simple move. However, as this would be an experiment, we could find out quite quickly what the potential gains and issues might be.

Delegitimizing Tax Havens—A more drastic measure would be to ban all use of offshore tax havens and tax avoidance schemes. A short grace window would be provided for citizens to bring their money back onshore to be subject to national taxation rules. Those who failed to conform would be faced with hefty penalties.

Higher Rate Taxes for a Fixed Period—Of course, the above measures may not work to provide the funds needed for the proposed measures. If so, then the targeted application of increased taxes to higher earning individuals and businesses could help provide the interim funding to finance the measures described above and in the previous chapter.

Bold Experiments and Courageous Leaders

There are no magic beans or money trees that can fund the costs of helping economies transition to the next model that serves the whole of society. At the same time, fundamental changes are taking place that will render people unemployed, and there is the potential for large-scale job loss if the more dramatic forecasts about the impacts of AI come to fruition. To avoid a medium- to long-term crisis, we need to be experimenting now with a range of policy measures to raise skill levels, generate new employment opportunities, and support those who lose their jobs in the transition process. Clearly these policy measures will require investments—these need to be offset against the potential costs of large-scale unemployment and a decline in global competitiveness. In the search to secure the future there are no guarantees—only bold experiments backed by leaders with the courage to pursue them.

- *How might we replace work with meaningful activity for the technologically unemployed?*
- *What issues beyond funding do we need to consider in making the transitions from this economy to future ones?*
- *What do we do to change the "sit and hope" mentality, and create an experimental mindset, that values trial and error?*

PART 3:
Human-Centered Cities

The Path to Smart—Mapping the Rise of Tomorrow's Smart Cities

Rohit Talwar, Steve Wells, and Alexandra Whittington

How might the smart city story evolve from hype to action in the coming decade?

The Drive for Smart and Sustainable Cities

The shift to smart infrastructures is not simply fashionable or aspirational; in many ways, it is a critical enabler of the future sustainability of human life on the planet. This goal requires a smooth transition to cities that are more efficient, less wasteful, and more conscious of the impacts of the individual upon the greater good. While there are many ways the future could unfold, here we explore a possible timeline for the evolution toward smart cities.

Near-Term Future (2018-2020)

We increasingly see carrot and stick approaches to both change people's habits and impact the travel decisions made by individuals and businesses. Local authorities are starting to penalize drivers who use fossil-fuel-based cars. For example, London has an increased Congestion Charge for the most polluting cars. Others are piloting or evaluating schemes that only allow car use on certain days or having entirely car-free days in certain parts of the city. Globally, metropolises could adopt these and other measures to encourage the use of public transportation.

To provide the data to underpin decision-making, cities could incrementally deploy a blanket of data collection sensors to monitor traffic and people. Main streets and intersections would become key nodes in the integrated network of a municipal mobility and transportation management system. The rise of the Internet of Things (IoT) could turn each sensor into a connected device able to analyze data in real time. Machine learning applications would evaluate and learn from the data to progressively suggest improvements to system operators.

In the drive for use of lower emissions vehicles, as the spread and reliability of charging infrastructures improves, more drivers are choosing electric vehicles. In the near future, lampposts, parking meters, and other street furniture could be retrofitted into charging stations—possibly powered by solar energy. Additionally, cities could collect data on energy usage and pollution levels on roads to help plan further developments—possibly even self-charging roadways, with Sweden the first to open one in April 2018.

Mid-Term Future (2021-2025)

Data could be collated from an evolving and expanding IoT, encompassing traffic lights, cameras, pollution sensors, and personal devices—all feeding cloud-based data stores. Crunching the data is becoming easier due to rampant growth in the use of algorithms, artificial intelligence (AI), and predictive software. Smart roads could feature effective ultra-efficient self-monitoring, self-powering, and maybe even self-repairing mechanisms that will characterize the modern smart city. Over time, as the constituent parts are implemented, the concepts of smart cities and smart infrastructure should feel less visionary and more strategic; "smart" may become the new normal. So, gradually, autonomous vehicles, intelligent street signs, robot and drone deliveries, and roadway repairs may become commonplace. At the same time, fossil-fuel-powered vehicles could be banned from increasing numbers of city centers.

Many city centers could change dramatically as technology enables more flexible working and changing employment patterns drive growth in the gig economy. For example, retail and business premises could be repurposed for residential and leisure use. The real estate footprint for many of the remaining stores may shrink as retailers opt for checkout-free models and digital displays with "click and collect" or home delivery options.

Long-Term Future (2026-2030)

The data collected through sensors and cameras could mean autonomous buses and trains (surface and subway) are managed through a transport control center that automatically matches services to demand. Encompassing automated road and rail signaling, and live predictive analytics to make best use of roads and rail tracks, the system could enable significant increases in public transport capacity and a reduction in privately owned vehicles.

Embedded sensors could monitor surface and sub-surface road conditions, with traffic flows monitored constantly against transport control center data on the maintenance history of all road surfaces. Predictive analysis of the data would then allow local authorities to undertake proactive maintenance before increased traffic flows cause roadway damage. This pre-emptive approach would reduce the need for lengthier and more extensive repairs later on and help minimize disruption to traffic flows.

The use of smart road technology to charge electric cars on the go could increase rapidly if the early pilots demonstrate cost savings for drivers and road maintenance authorities. In parallel, solar pavement panels and kinetic walkways could capture energy, allowing streets to power themselves. Sunlight and pedestrian usage forecasting tools could help determine potential solar and kinetic supply patterns. This would help energy companies manage peaks and troughs in demand through a decentralized smart energy generation and storage infrastructure.

As positive experiences with autonomous vehicles accumulate, we should see the first cluster of municipalities and nations such as

Norway and Sweden to outlaw human drivers because the risks are too great and errors too high compared to the safety record of autonomous cars.

The Smart City Leadership Challenge

We are moving from hype to the potential for positive action on smart cities. A combination of environmental pressures, technological progress, and a concerned and active citizenry are laying down the challenge for city leaders and planners. The issue for leaders in particular is to ensure that in the transition to tomorrow's smart city, the citizens are the biggest winners, and the impacts are managed for those who might lose out. Ultimately, the goal is to ensure the city visions and strategies are centered on harnessing technology's capabilities to ensure sustainable, livable, and vibrant cities that enhance the quality of life for citizens.

- *What's driving smart city thinking today—citizen needs, environmental concerns, economic pressures, or technology promise?*
- *How can we build genuine citizen engagement into the planning of smart cities and what behavioral changes are required to deliver the full potential of smart city visions?*
- *How robust is our smart city thinking—how valid are the underlying long-term assumptions and how do our plans hold up under a range of possible economic and environmental scenarios?*

A version of this chapter was originally published in Tech Donut under the title "Tomorrow's World: The Evolution of Smart Cities."

The Intelligence Premium—Smart Models for Smarter Living in the Smartest Cities

Rohit Talwar, Steve Wells, and Alexandra Whittington

How might exponential technologies help us design and deliver an enhanced city living experience?

Unlocking the Intelligence in Our Cities

Across the disciplines of architecture, engineering, and construction, three forces are coming together to drive the next waves of opportunity in the built environment—namely people, intelligent systems, and smart city concepts. At the core of the opportunity is the notion of creating truly livable environments for humanity, designed using intelligent tools, and delivered and managed through a range of technologies that will help us bring smart city visions to fruition.

Livable means creating cities that are human, vibrant, forward looking, functional, smart, and sustainable. The core tools underpinning their design will be those that can amplify human intelligence on a massive scale to interpret, predict, and create solutions based on the immense volumes of information about life in the city that is being gathered daily. Holding it all together will be highly interconnected smart environments where people, governments, and businesses can live and work together effectively using emerging and exponentially improving technologies such as big data, the Internet of Things (IoT), cloud computing, hyperconnectivity, artificial intelligence (AI), robots, drones, autonomous green vehicles, 3D/4D printing, smart materials, and renewable energy.

Aligning Stakeholder Goals and Visions

While the potential of smart cities is exciting, in practice it can be very hard to develop a clear, inclusive and universally supported future vision and strategy which delivers on everyone's needs and leaves no one behind. Part of the challenge is that goals are not always aligned across the stakeholders and, at the same time, every sector is being disrupted and all our assumptions are being challenged. Hence, few can see what the needs of their business, locality, or family might be in the next 12-24 months let alone the five- to fifteen-year period over which a true smart city infrastructure might be rolled out. However, that's exactly what we must do. City governments have to create inclusive processes that firstly inform citizens about the forces shaping the future and the possibilities and challenges on the horizon, and then engage the population in an open dialogue about the kind of future we want to create.

This is where architects, engineers, and construction specialists have an important role to play. They can help us explore and model what a livable city could mean to its people and contribute to the articulation of a clear vision. They can also offer insights on the ways in which the physical, digital, and human elements of a smart city infrastructure might be delivered and managed.

Technologies Transforming the Design and Implementation of Tomorrow's Cities

Increasingly, the tools available to architects, engineers, and construction specialists are becoming more sophisticated and intelligent. From visioning to construction planning, increasing use is being made of the analytic and predictive capabilities of AI. At the same time, the digital drawing board is coming to life through virtual and augmented reality (VR/AR) to create immersive experiences throughout the design, planning, and construction process. Hence, the impacts of a development on the surrounding ecosystem can be modeled to much greater detail than ever before. For example, the implications of a range of events from day-to-day emergencies to natural disasters and security incidents can be simulated to help ensure the robustness and workability of designs and to provide greater confidence in the rigor of risk assessments.

Over time, the capability of the technologies will continue to amaze and astound. For example, the combination of 3D printed structures and rapid building construction may lead to a more agile form of urban planning than can exist today. The spread and embedding of sensors and detectors could also provide vital insights into city life—indicating emerging needs for different parts of the city—from waste collection to traffic control. This idea of treating the physical infrastructure more like software with built-to-suit-and-adapt homes, offices, and public spaces might create cities which respond in almost real time to a range of behavioral fluctuations. Hence, smart cities might evolve in much the same way as businesses add and withdraw software applications, functionality, storage capacity, processing power, and communications bandwidth to suit demand fluctuations. As a practical advantage, this might mean that big events like the Olympic Games could be accommodated rapidly with a largely temporary pop-up infrastructure that then disappears a few weeks after the event, rather than leave a permanent footprint and the costly challenge of ensuring the continued usage and upkeep of facilities.

Another example of these technology tools on steroids is the emerging range of IoT-based home automation and protection products. For example, USA start-up Vayyar is experimenting with the use of 3D imaging to see through walls—meaning no structure would be impenetrable. This omniscient form of surveillance could put building designers and architects in a curious position of having to decide on the aesthetics and purpose of non-load-bearing walls that are technically invisible.

This emerging wave of intelligent cities is typically being designed to enable smart management decisions—capturing and interpreting massive amounts of data about the population and its behavioral patterns, such as water use and traffic flows. This information gathering via different forms of surveillance results in what is called big data. Within five years, the deployment of ever-smarter AI and advanced analytics will mean this function could be completely automated. The data can be collated from a constantly evolving and expanding IoT of devices as described earlier—all literally feeding giant data stores held in the cloud.

A leading example of a smart city in operation is Singapore, with its constantly evolving "city brain." This backbone of technologies helps control pollution, monitor traffic, allocate parking, communicate with citizens, and even issue traffic fines. Singapore's "brain" is also attempting to modify human behavior; for example, one system rewards drivers for using recommended mapped routes, and punishes those who do not. Ultimately, Singapore's planners hope to discourage driving, and steer commuters toward greater use of public transportation. The city is planning for a physical environment of 100 million "smart objects" including smart traffic lights, lampposts, sensors, and cameras on its roadways, which will be used to monitor and enforce laws.

Integrating the Internet of Things

In order for everything from air conditioning to parking meters to function in a smart city, an array of high-tech data gathering gadgetry must be hooked up to the IoT—including cameras, microphones, voice recognition devices, and a variety of sensors and gauges. Vendors and planners are already beginning to explore and model the possibilities presented by this trend toward total data capture. For example, a case study from India suggests that light poles along the highways can offer both smart city and connectivity solutions. In addition to helping monitor road conditions, the light poles could be fitted as high-speed data connections.

Data is a critical element of the smart city/smart road future. However, because this option will further expand the relationship between internet service providers, surveillance, and private business including advertisers, there are several issues around privacy to be considered.

Naturally, most would want the information from smart cities and roads to be used to keep citizens moving, healthy, and protected. However, should companies then be allowed to target users with adverts based on this information when it was collected for other purposes?

Smart Roads and Smart Mobility Management

Within and between the smart cities of the future, smart roads in particular are where planners can put into effect many of the ultra-efficient mechanisms that best characterize their vision. In general, the concepts around smart cities, smart roads, and smart infrastructure are becoming less hype-laden and more strategic and sustainable by the day. As cities grow in size and importance to the global economy, it will be increasingly important that they adopt the most innovative and forward-thinking design and sustainability ideas—particularly around road infrastructure. As a smart future unfolds, three important new technologies—big data, the IoT, and renewable energy—are being used in parallel to transform the day-to-day.

South Korea, for example, is planning an entire network of smart roads by 2020. This will include battery-charging stations for electric vehicles (EVs) as well as infrastructure to handle autonomous vehicles. The introduction of driverless vehicles requires roads to be transformed into information superhighways as vehicles will need to communicate with each other and the city infrastructure. Mapping, traffic signals, and safety regulations, for instance, are all parts of the physical and digital infrastructure that will have to become highly coordinated for autonomous vehicles to function safely and effectively.

All this data will enable decisions that make efficient use of space, fuel, water, electricity, and waste products, with an emphasis on sustainability. For example, anticipating major traffic jams to provide alternative routes—reducing journey time, fuel consumption, and the impact on the city infrastructure.

The smart city movement now afoot has the potential to transform the organization of people and physical objects in a way that transcends urban development as we know it. The shift to smart infrastructure is not simply fashionable or aspirational; in many ways, it appears to be a critical enabler of the future sustainability of cities. It can be argued that the future of human life on the planet rests on a smooth transition to cities that are more efficient, less wasteful, and more conscious of the impacts of the individual upon the greater good. This may include a range of new negotiations along the boundaries of individual freedom and privacy; for example, replacing human drivers with self-driving cars in the hope of preventing death and injury in auto accidents, increasing traffic efficiency, and reducing environmental impacts. Similarly, to reach municipal conservation goals, we might have to agree to invasive monitoring of waste generation, energy, and water use in the home. These are the kinds of tensions that future planners will need to wrestle with on a continuous basis.

The challenge and opportunity for leaders, planners, architects, engineers, and construction specialists are clear. The smart city shouldn't be an apocalyptic future where citizens are stripped of their free will, and we cannot be seduced by the technoprogressive view that the pursuit of smart roads will lead to utopia. However, it is now possible to create and deliver a city vision with citizens at its heart—one that is enabled by forward-thinking infrastructure planning coupled with judicious use of enabling technologies. A well-thought-through vision, enabled by a robust and well-executed smart city model, could provide a foundation stone for the next stage of our development, where science and technology are genuinely harnessed in service of creating a better place for current and future city residents.

- *How can we develop the required forward-thinking managerial and leadership capabilities within cities and among those who design and build them?*
- *How can we ensure that those involved keep the citizen at the center of strategies and projects delivering our smart city visions?*
- *Which concepts and technologies are most central to bringing about the smart vision for your city?*

A version of this chapter was originally published in AEC Magazine under the title "The Future of Smart Cities."

The Future of Multimodal Transport in a Self-Driving World

Rohit Talwar, Steve Wells, Alexandra Whittington, and Helena Calle

What are the scenarios for multimodal transportation in a self-driving future?

Planning Transport for a World of Unknowns

City transport planners around the world are faced with an incredibly complex task of determining the transport infrastructure for the next 20-50 years. The complexity derives from the need to determine the transport and supporting infrastructure required for modes of transport that don't all exist, carrying people who may not yet have been born, working in jobs and industries that may not yet have been created, with huge uncertainty on the resulting mobility implications. Now, the likelihood is that mass transportation—especially into city centers—at peak times will be required for at least the next two decades. However, planners are challenged by the fact that mobility patterns could change quite quickly. So, for example, economic growth could drive job creation and a demand for more transport into key work locations. However, a rapid rise in the pace of automation could see many jobs eliminated with a dramatic impact on transport demand.

One big excitement factor is autonomous vehicles which could potentially offer a more personalized service. For example, could autonomous vehicles pick travelers up from their homes and be loaded onto trains at the station? When the train reaches the city center terminal, the "train" would break into component vehicle parts and take each traveler to their end destination, thereby providing a "first mile/last mile" solution. While such developments may be a decade or more from fruition, planners need to be thinking of these possibilities now to avoid the need for costly infrastructure rework projects in the future.

Another interesting development we've been looking at is flying taxis. Following successful trials of single person passenger drones in 2017, commercial services are due to be launched in China and the UAE in the next few years. The technology is slated to continue to improve and, around the world, by 2023 more than 20 countries might have licensed the use of both single and multiple occupant passenger drones. From a planner's perspective, again it is hard to determine the possible requirements for such services which may not even be part of current government strategy or have regulatory approval.

Trends Driving Multimodal Transport Thinking

One of the forces that is clearly important to transport is the autonomous driving trend that permits robotic devices and artificial intelligence to complete the supply chain. The future thrust toward self-driving cars is a key one to watch. A number of powerful separate trends are combining here to challenge our thinking about the different possible future multimodal scenarios we must prepare for. These include the automation of transportation, changing commuting behaviors, the evolution of delivery/supply chains, the application of AI to transport planning, the growth of home working, automation of jobs, and changing patterns of disposable income. There are also questions here about what might be the new opportunities and risks resulting from multimodal transport for global companies, and what might be the resulting innovative future growth strategies in multimodal transport? The big risk here is that we under- or over-provide and invest either too little or too much in transport infrastructure relative to likely demand. Predicting the exact volumes and transport mix is a difficult challenge under current economic and technological uncertainty.

The Use of Mobility Scenarios

Our approach to de-risking the planning process is to envision a range of possible future scenarios to help identify alternative strategy approaches. For example, one scenario we envisioned is Data Drives the Future. In this 2030 scenario, Transport for London (TfL) runs Greater London's multimodal transport network using a fully integrated AI-based Travel and Transport Management System (TTMS). Vast amounts of data are processed using human expertise, AI-based transport infrastructure planning and traffic management algorithms, and predictive analysis—drawing on sensors in roads, pavements, and public transport access points.

What does this future look like? In this scenario, traffic and pedestrian flows have grown exponentially smoother, transport's environmental impacts have declined dramatically, and London is ranked first globally on mobility. A single control center automatically manages and matches services to demand—combining autonomous buses and surface and subway trains, and road and rail signaling. Live predictive analytics allows greater use of road and track space. Autonomous boats ply their trade on the Thames from Putney in the west to Woolwich Royal Arsenal in the east. An automated fail-safe mode restricts public access to capacity-sensitive areas like underground stations and riverboat piers.

Manual drive cars of all fuel types would still exist, but only autonomous electrically powered vehicles are permitted in the city center. A constant flow of data between autonomous vehicles (their current location, destination, and purpose of the journey) and the central system would be used to re-route traffic around congested areas. The system also gives priority to public transport and emergency services. The system's associated app provides pedestrians' personal digital assistants with navigational information.

This is all made possible by embedded road sensors monitoring surface and sub-surface conditions. Traffic types and flows are constantly monitored against the TTMS' comprehensive historic road status database—proactively undertaking maintenance. This reduces requirements for lengthier and more extensive subsequent repairs, minimizing traffic disruption by accurately re-routing transport resources during repairs, maintenance, and emergency situations, and predicting the implications.

These scenarios combine a range of driving forces on traveler behavior and demand and allow for the creation of alternative storylines about how the future could play out. There is also a strong element of visioning—articulating what we'd like to see happen in each scenario. This type of approach lets planners and policy-makers prepare for a range of possibilities and bring flexibility into the definitions of tangible goals and visions under different prevailing circumstances. In each case, the goal is still to serve humanity as best we can but the resources available and strategies we adopt might vary dramatically from scenario to scenario. These scenarios then become the basis of communication with leaders—enabling them to make better informed and more robust decisions.

The Impacts of Multimodal Transport on Individuals and Society

The personal example of multimodal transport that individuals might notice most easily is that of changes in how consumer goods are obtained and the resulting impact on personal time and expenditure. In future, the use of multimodal delivery services could see drones as one of the modes of "last mile" transport, as Amazon and Domino's and others have experimented with.

A drone could deliver a pizza directly from the kitchen, or packages from a centralized drone port, where the goods have already been delivered by truck, train, or airplane. Another strategy would be the increased use of shared autonomous vehicles (such as Uber) for both consumer and goods transport. Passengers and goods might travel together to the same destinations, allowing for passengers to have the option to ride free and act as de facto delivery persons.

In terms of public transport, might train stations that are less crowded outside peak travel times host pop-up digital shopping malls? Autonomous and shared transport implies greater convenience and ease, so perhaps people will have more time on their hands to browse and shop during commutes. Conversely, train stations may become places where people can pick up consumer goods en route to their homes or jobs. This could transform their commute into a profitable or time-saving activity, or at least eat away at some of their personal transportation costs by becoming part of the supply chain.

Challenges Posed by Multimodal Transport for Governments

Clearly there is a major challenge around planning for the desired capacity, funding the infrastructure, building it, and coordinating schedules across the participants in the ecosystem. In terms of self-driving transport (trains, buses, cars, and taxis), one question government and local planners should be asking is "Will parking soon be obsolete?" In 10-15 years, the idea of a stationary vehicle may be an anachronism. In future smart cities, self-driving vehicles should be enabled by data to orchestrate smooth mobility with almost no stopping required, other than to let passengers on and off. Self-driving cars are but one current in a larger wave of change sweeping us toward this vision; another is the erosion of car ownership.

The rise of endeavors like Uber, Lyft, and Ola Car have popularized mass ride sharing, and it is imaginable that in a smart city environment, such programs could become the norm. The environmental and economic benefits, like cleaner air, and less traffic, might encourage creation of more pedestrian areas and green spaces—improving public health. Most of all, the ability to creatively reclaim spaces that are now devoted to parked cars could enhance the quality of life in cities, a key consideration in terms of the legacy for future generations. Policies that engender these changes in transportation can be win-wins for elected officials. Another challenge that multimodal transport poses for governments is how to implement a more commercial approach to offer a more attractive service for customers. A fluent dialogue between the governments and multimodal transport companies is essential to face the challenge of providing an appealing transport service.

Conclusion—Planning as Scenario Visioning

The rise of autonomous vehicles seems inevitable; what we can't yet determine is what proportion of the total vehicle fleet will be self-driving, or what demand might look like. Equally we have little certainty about the future shape of the workforce and hence what the patterns of traveler demand might be. Given the scale of the uncertainties, planners must look to the use of a hybrid scenario thinking/visioning approach to articulate different possible driver combinations and outline the resulting multimodal transport strategies that they might pursue under each scenario. The key here is to put the citizen at the heart of the process and to be clear what the benefits and downsides are for the population in each case.

- *Can transport business models expand to include the provision of a "one stop shop" door to door service, maybe by running fleets of autonomous vehicles that can utilize rail infrastructure as well as roads?*
- *What futuristic uses can rail companies put their infrastructure to? For example, could track routes become autonomous drone highways?*
- *How can train companies work with bus companies, hire car providers, and hotels to integrate traveler information and travel needs? What AI-led data sources can enhance the planning and provision of integrated travel services?*

This chapter is based on an interview given to DB Cargo magazine.

Housing 2030
—A Better Way of Living?

Rohit Talwar, Steve Wells, Alexandra Whittington, and Maria Romero

How might intelligence technologies shape our homes and lifestyles?

Smarter Living–An Abundance of Possibilities

There are numerous visions of what the cities of the future could look like, but a core idea about the future of cities is the notion that in the coming decades, urban environments will be enveloped by a digital blanket of sensors, devices, and cloud connected data which makes life run smoothly. Disruptive technologies ranging from renewable energy to artificial intelligence (AI), blockchain, 3D printing, and the Internet of Things (IoT) are being brought together to deliver a newly enhanced city living experience: the smart city. The core concepts encompass all of the key elements of what enable cities to function effectively—from traffic control and environmental protection to the management of energy, sanitation, healthcare, security, and buildings.

Future smart cities promise to harmonize the benefits of contemporary "smart" technologies in order to provide a high quality of life. As the infrastructure upon which smart cities rest begins to take shape, the impact on homes is a critical strategic issue for estate and property professionals. How does life in smart cities translate to the city's most personal microcosm, the home? How might it impact notions such as property leases and rental—could entirely new concepts emerge to replace them? Could the technology enable properties to lease themselves on the open market—charging literally by the minute or hour? To what extent are renters and buyers willing to give up some degree of privacy and free will to live in a smart city? Will homes be state-owned, privately owned, or organized on a sharing economy model? Smart cities will have a direct but as yet unknown potential impact on the world of property letting.

At the occupant level, how does the prospect of living smart appeal to customers today, and what will it be like ten years from now? Who will be responsible for smart sensors and data—if it breaks, or malfunctions, who will fix it? Above all, how will humanity be preserved in a future where technology is involved in every step of the day, even within the privacy of home?

A Shared Vision

City governments have to create inclusive processes to encourage citizens to join conversations about the forces shaping the future and the possibilities and challenges on the horizon. In particular, it will be essential to engage the population in dialogue about the desired future. Involvement might be best coordinated on a local/neighborhood level, for example—coming to agreement on what a livable city means, and how to attract jobs and support a constant flow of industries of the future.

Alongside the visioning role, local communities must have a voice in articulating a clear preference around education, environment, public services, access to justice, city administration, and civic engagement. These pillars then provide the guiding requirements which will in turn influence the design of smart infrastructure. City residents, as individual stakeholders or in coalitions, could provide a much-needed check on the powers of the smart city policy-makers and technology service providers. The quality of a smart city's engagement might actually have a direct bearing on its popularity and hence property rental values.

Big Data—A Fine Line between Observation and Surveillance

Smart cities are designed to inform decisions by capturing massive amounts of data about the population and its patterns, such as water use and traffic flows. This information gathering results in what is called big data, and it is essentially gathered via surveillance. There can also be voluntary efforts to collect information, but the ease and affordability of sensors, AI, and advanced analytics in the future will mean this function can be completely automated. The data can be collated from almost any city infrastructure, encompassing traffic lights and cameras, pollution sensors, building control systems, individual homes, and personal devices—all literally feeding giant data stores held in the cloud. The ability to crunch all this data is becoming easier due to rampant growth in the use of algorithms, AI, and predictive software running on networks of high performance computing and storage devices. The availability of such near-complete data might prove extremely valuable in creating true comparisons of the environmental footprint, energy efficiency, and safety of homes and hence of rental values.

While the technological capacity is nearly in place, is there a matching political will to use it effectively? A number of questions need ironing out concerning freedom, surveillance, and privacy in smart cities. Interesting developments recently, such as court admission of evidence collected by a smart home assistant, remind us that smart technologies could evolve in ways that could jeopardize human rights and social justice.

Internet of Things (IoT)—Always Connected

Smart cities rely on advanced technology to make sense of massive collections of information. Indeed, the amount of information on the internet is expected to grow exponentially as a result of the IoT. Essentially IoT means that everything ("things")—and potentially everyone—will become beacons and data collection devices, gathering data on ambient and behavioral patterns from its surroundings and from the information it is fed, and networking all this data via the cloud.

Hence, after data, the IoT is the second driving force behind the rise of smart infrastructure: in order for everything from air conditioning to parking meters to function in a smart city, the use of microphones, sensors, voice recognition, and all sorts of other high-tech gadgetry must be hooked up to the IoT.

In terms of the private home, it is conceivable that the Alexa or Google Home will become connected to public IoTs in order to communicate everything from home energy usage to ordering fresh groceries. The future of the home may be wired for calling up a self-driving taxi when it is time to leave for work, for example. Smart home products that are already in place, such as security and temperature/ambience automation (e.g., Nest) will be able to "talk" to the police department in case of an intruder or unlock the door for expected guests using facial recognition cameras at the entryways. Homeowners will find themselves becoming a hub in a city-wide communication network— one of millions communicating to the same central "brain" of the city. What might the implications be for property rental models when we can access such "perfect information" about a home, one's neighbors, the neighborhood, and every facet of the lives of the individual?

Sustainability–Low-Impact Strategies

Finally, all this data and awareness will enable decisions that make the best possible use of space, fuel, energy, water, electricity, and all resources, with an emphasis on sustainability. For example, a clear smart city priority is being able to anticipate big traffic jams and provide alternative routes to save time, fuel, and reduce impact on the city infrastructure itself. Limiting waste is a very logical outcome and benefit of the merging of big data, AI, and IoT which feed into the rise of smart infrastructure.

Electric vehicles (EVs) are growing their market foothold; hence the charging concerns related to EVs are gaining urgency in the eyes of many policy-makers and planners. Interestingly, the car companies themselves are exploring similar options as they place their stakes on sustainable solutions beyond transportation: BMW and Nissan have released home energy batteries that can extend the life of an electric car battery as an in-home renewable energy source, even capable of storing solar energy. With a view to reducing parking requirements, could access to a shared EV become an essential requirement for new properties and rental offerings?

Eventually, with a growing array of such distributed power solutions, a centralized energy distribution grid for homes and businesses may not be necessary. In the next decades, homes could run on their own energy stores, and preserve enough to share, sell, or store for their own later use. The homeowner would no longer depend on a power company to provide electricity, and the home would reach a "net zero" level of ecological impact; giving back more (if not less) than it takes from nature. How might rental prices be affected by a home's capacity to generate income from electricity generation?

Cities Get Smart

It can be argued that the future of human life on the planet rests on a smooth transition to cities that are more efficient, less wasteful, and more conscious of the impacts of the individual upon the greater good. This may include a range of new negotiations along the boundaries of freedom and privacy: for example, allowing self-driving cars to replace human drivers in the hope of preventing death and injury in auto accidents, increasing traffic efficiency, and removing environmental impacts. Similarly, to reach municipal conservation goals, we might have to agree to invasive monitoring of waste generation, energy, and water use in the home. These are the kinds of tensions that future planners will need to wrestle with on a continuous basis. Furthermore, they form a set of novel and emerging concerns for future home renters and buyers. For the letting industry, a key question arises around the role it should play in contributing to smart city visions and developing smart rental models that take advantage of all the continuously updated data and insights we will have about properties and their all-round performance.

Ultimately, this is about creating cities that work for people. A thoughtful vision of the future enabled by a robust and well-executed smart city model could provide a foundation for channeling science and technology advances into the creation of a very human future in the city of tomorrow.

- *How do we define the boundary between smarter lifestyles and invasion of privacy when it varies for each of us?*
- *What are the critical services you would want in your future home?*
- *How do we ensure that every lifestyle choice improves our environmental footprint?*

A version of this chapter was originally published in The Negotiator under the title "Housing 2030—Living Smarter."

City Farming—Beyond Vertical Solutions

April Koury

How might indoor farming solutions deliver the food requirements of a growing and more affluent urban population?

The City Farming Opportunity

When I see drawings of future utopian cityscapes, the images often involve tall, gleaming glass skyscrapers interspersed with fat vertical columns of greenery running the entire height of the structure. After all, it's estimated that close to 70% of the world's population will live in cities by 2050, and those vertical gardens will help feed hungry urban mouths. What we're starting to realize, however, is that farming within cities can go beyond vertical—with some creative engineering and a touch of science we could be reclaiming and repurposing derelict city sites in order to provide ample amounts of fresh food to urban populations.

From Vertical to Containerized—Innovative Urban Farming Solutions

Amazing feats of large-scale city farming have already begun in abandoned factories. Set up inside a repurposed industrial building in Chicago, The Plant is a complete food system which grows vegetables and freshwater fish, brews Kombucha and beer, and produces enough energy from the by-products of these processes to light and heat the entire plant. The world's largest indoor farm has been built within one of Sony's old semiconductor factories in Japan. The farm currently ships out 10,000 heads of lettuce a day.

In areas where food system projects as space-consuming as The Plant will not be feasible, "contained farming" could be a solution. PlantLab, a Dutch firm, has developed a contained system in which crops are grown indoors under very specific LED lighting conditions, and the crops use roughly one tenth of the water of a traditional greenhouse. On an even smaller scale, The Farmery repurposes shipping containers into mini farms, where food is grown and sold in the same location. Hydroponically watered herbs and vegetables grow on the outside of the containers, and gourmet mushrooms are grown in the dark interiors. Customers simply walk in and harvest their own produce from the walls, and the shipping containers are portable and can be set up in small lots.

Self-Sustaining Ecosystems

Ultimately, these examples point to a future in which we could be able to set up entirely self-sustained farming ecosystems within urban neighborhoods, reducing the environmental impacts of both traditional farming and produce delivery. In this vision, because the majority of larger urban crops will be grown indoors, pests will be nonexistent thus removing the use of pesticides, and disease and contamination could be prevented easily. Farmers will have total control over temperature, humidity, and irrigation, reducing water usage to an estimated 1% of outdoor farming. Controlled lighting will optimize plant growth, thus growing crops at a faster rate than traditional farming. Contained farms additionally offer the option to grow food almost anywhere including in lightless underground structures.

What we're beginning to see is the evolution of farming—acres and acres of flat, irrigated cropland open to the elements simply waste too much space, water, and energy to meet the needs of our growing population. Repurposing old city sites into new city farms holds the promise of providing abundant, fresh, locally grown foods for future urbanites worldwide.

- *What are the key benefits and potential downsides of pursuing urban farming solutions?*
- *How might consumers respond to the idea of food grown in vertical or containerized farms?*
- *What practical steps could be taken to accelerate the adoption of urban farming—should local government planners insist that all supermarkets of a certain size include a localized farming solution?*

PART 4:
People, Jobs, Capability

Choosing a Human Path to the Future

Rohit Talwar and Alexandra Whittington

What future roles can we envisage for people in an automated world and what might the implications be for human-to-human relations?

Reframing Humanity's Place in a Technological World

As we look at the changes shaping our world and the pace of technological advancement, some very big questions start to arise:

- *Are humans irrelevant to the future of business?*
- *What role should humans play when machines can outperform them in most tasks?*
- *How should society prepare for an unknowable future?*

There are five important dimensions that we must address as part of securing humanity's future in an automated world and ensuring that the advances in technology are used to serve humanity—not replace it.

1. *Reframing Society*–We are reaching a truly dramatic point in human history where a number of exponential technologies are being combined to deliver radical performance improvements. A powerful mix of unleashed imaginations applied to disruptive technologies is catalyzing a possibility revolution across every

aspect of human life, society, government, and business. As a result, in the next few years, society will be challenged to confront fundamental issues that go to the core of what it means to be human. Advances in science and technology will test every assumption we have about how our world works and the purpose of humans within it. For example, artificial intelligence (AI) already outperforms humans in many domains, and the possibility of artificial superintelligence, or constantly learning and evolving systems, could result in machines capable of overtaking human capabilities—ultimately even in so-called soft skills such as empathy, intuition, and creativity.

2. *Humanity 2.0*–Advances in cognitive enhancement drugs and "nootropic" supplements, electronic brain stimulation techniques, genetics, age extension treatments, 3D printed limbs and organs, and body worn exoskeletons, have given rise to the notion of enhancing the human brain and body well beyond the limits of natural evolutionary processes. Indeed, many leaders in the field of AI are fierce advocates of "Transhumanism" as the next stage of human evolution—arguing that if humans want to keep up with AI, we ourselves will have to become machines—embedding technology in our brains and bodies to give us similar levels of processing power. So, is there a meaningful future for version 1.0 humans in this brave new and enhanced world that the technoprogressives would have us believe is the only viable way forward for humanity?

3. *The Risks of Automation*–The challenge here lies in our choices as decision makers and the value we place on human attributes that machines cannot as yet replicate. Clearly, automation has many benefits such as cost efficiency, consistency, speed, and accuracy. Many firms will inevitably choose to place their faith in computer systems, automating wherever possible. Such a philosophy is common in new technology ventures where the heart of the business is embedded in its code. Some are already creating Decentralized Autonomous Organizations (DAO)—entities that have no employees and exist entirely in software.

The potential rewards of widespread digitization of an enterprise are well-covered in the business media, but what isn't talked about enough is the spectrum of risks presented by automation, especially to well-established organizations. Companies run the risk of dehumanizing and becoming identical to others in their industry—losing whatever their distinctive edge might be and commoditizing themselves in the process. Furthermore, the more we choose to embed all that we do in software, the easier it becomes for competitors to replicate our offering and go a step further at a slightly lower price—locking us into a deadly race to the bottom on prices, revenues, and profitability.

4. *What Differentiates Humans from Machines?*–The challenge is to harness AI and other disruptive technologies such as robotics, cloud computing, the Internet of Things (IoT), blockchain, and hyperconnectivity as power tools to support and unleash human potential. At least for some time to come, what differentiates a company will be very human characteristics—the quality of its ideas, strategies, and business models; its community relations; the ability to spot and exploit opportunities or address risks quickly; handling exceptional customer needs; creating new products and services; building deep connections within and outside the organization; how it navigates external developments such as regulatory requirements; and how well it manages change. These remain very human traits which machines cannot yet replicate. New technologies can play a powerful role in supporting the people performing these tasks and automating more routine work to free up time for us to undertake these higher-level human functions. Organizations that see AI as simply a way to cut back on staffing are missing the point.

5. *Unleashing Human Potential*–Artificial intelligence is increasing business productivity, knowledge, and efficiency, but humans cannot be written off just yet. In the insurance industry, while chatbots are emerging at the customer interface, there is a concern that AI is not yet at the point where machines can respond appropriately to distressed customers, an unfortunately common

emotional state due to the nature of matters insurance companies deal with. Artificial intelligence offers a chance to re-humanize the workforce by providing more time to use our talents and softer skills and emotional intelligence while offloading less sensitive tasks to machines. Obviously, we will need training and support to help us step into these intellectually and emotionally more demanding roles.

Tomorrow's Opportunities

As individuals, managers, leaders, investors, and politicians we crave certainty and predictability. We want the future served up to us on a plate with the timelines, impacts, and solutions clearly defined. Reality is far messier and changes constantly—the only certainties are that: i) ignoring the emerging future will store up problems; and ii) trying to apply yesterday's or today's solutions to the future's challenges will almost certainly fail. What we do know is that the situation will evolve rapidly as the pace of technology quickens, and as businesses seek to act faster to take advantage of what's on offer and respond to potential competitive threats. A wide range of professions from sales person and school teacher to investment banker, risk assessor, claims analyst, plumber, and bus driver will see technology emerge that can enhance or even replace their roles.

Within five years, it is reasonable to foresee quite significant shifts in the types of jobs available, the skills levels required, and a shortening duration for those roles. On a ten-year time frame, we could reasonably expect to see widespread automation, a dramatic reduction of the jobs that exist today, new roles emerging in new firms and in existing businesses as they seek to stay competitive, and educationally, a degree or its equivalent could become a minimum entry requirement for 80% or more of all new jobs created.

Navigating the Messy Middle

So, what about the messy middle between here and the end of the next decade? In the short term, the picture will be confused—certain firms and industries will accelerate rapidly toward an "employee light" model. Other sectors will see temporary skills shortages until the processes become more automated and the machines learn to code themselves. In professions ranging from machine learning specialists to quantity surveyors, we can see a near-term skills shortage with supply lagging demand. This represents an immediate opportunity to retrain people for these in-demand roles.

However, as the process of automation accelerates and the way we work evolves over the next 5-10 years, we might see skill shortages erode and the emergence of very different ways of achieving an outcome. For example, an autonomous vehicle might automatically fine its driver should they choose to take the wheel while drunk or override the speed limit. The vehicle might also self-insure—sharing the risk across the pool of autonomous cars on the road. These smart cars might also drive themselves to the shop for repairs—carried out by a team of robots and drones. These changes wouldn't so much re-engineer the work of solicitors, courtrooms, garages, and insurance firms—rather the activities, associated tasks, and related jobs might be eliminated completely.

The Emergence of New Jobs

Over time, new jobs will arise with the emergence of new activities, businesses, and sectors. For example, human augmentation will require a range of new skills, possibly combined into hybrid roles that draw on chemistry, biology, electro-mechanical engineering, psychology, and counseling. Highly trained workers will also be required in sectors such as smart materials, 3D/4D printing, autonomous car manufacture, superfast construction, environmental protection and remediation, renewable energy, and care of the elderly. In insurance, the skills of the next generation risk assessor will need to encompass a wider range of disciplines to handle the new fields of science and technology coming to market.

At a more fundamental level, we could see a rise in teacher numbers if countries see education as a priority. In parallel, the opportunities in basic and applied R&D could blossom if nations and firms increase their research investments in search of future growth. We could also see a massive growth in small businesses and mentoring roles as people seek to take control of their own destiny. Increased leisure time could drive a resurgence of opportunities in the creative arts, with an expansion of training provision for would-be actors, dancers, painters, and poets. Finally, the stress associated with job displacement due to technology could result in a growing need both for mental health support for people while still in the job and for care in the community for those with mental health issues resulting from the loss of their job.

Redefining Jobs

One of the most important things to keep in mind is that there could be many new definitions of the term "job" in the next 5-20 years. A job today is still a fundamental assumption and organizing principle in most Western nations—even if it is being eroded, governments still plan on that basis. A job today is a means to earn money by achieving a set of given tasks. For some it is more—a calling to fulfill one's purpose and give meaning and structure to our lives. For others, it is a means to an end—be that paying for our next meal or providing the money to realize our materialistic, experiential, or spiritual desires.

So, as work is gradually and then more rapidly automated away, what becomes of the job? What might a job look like in 2027? Will it still be a "production" role delivering measurable daily outputs, or will a job imply a more creative human activity? Will it still be what people do all day? Conceivably, AI could remove aspects of jobs that tend to be considered "work" while emphasizing the parts of a job that make it a social and enriching activity. Will we have moved to a guaranteed or universal basic income (UBI), with people having the choice over where they spend their time, from being a server in a restaurant to taking part in community building restoration projects? The link between how we spend our time and the income we receive might be broken in less than a decade, meaning people could have more autonomy over how they use their time and energy than ever before.

The technology we adopt today will also allow companies to increase their options in terms of achieving outcomes. While Company A might use AI to reduce the size and budget of their legal department, they might in turn boost their investment in the IT and HR departments to ensure they have the right technological capacities and that the attorneys and others they hire are absolutely the right fit. Company B might implement AI to reduce the number of customer service calls routed to human operators, but they could re-invest the salary savings on bringing in trainers and facilitators to raise digital literacy, emotional intelligence, critical thinking ability, and communication skills across the firm. New training curricula would require new positions to run the programs, e.g. "Director of Lifelong Learning." In this case, a job might be more akin to an education: you would leave it smarter and better-prepared than when you arrived.

Time for Extraordinary Leadership

Aside from jobs, bringing AI into the workplace successfully will require new workplace leadership styles. The leaders of AI-powered organizations will face unprecedented challenges which will test their people skills and emotional intelligence. "Warm" and highly relatable individuals might be in demand to offset the extent of "cold" automation within an organization. Of course, this won't be universally true—for some, the ultimate goal is to create the DAO, and for them the pursuit of automation and a workforce led by "robot overlords" is just a stepping stone to the employee-free business of the future. However, at present, humanity seems to be prevailing to some degree, and total digitization seems unlikely to become a genuine threat for the majority of larger global businesses in the near term.

Indeed, in a world where there's a risk of automation, dehumanization, and commoditization proceeding hand in hand, those who put people first could find themselves better positioned to create, innovate, adapt, evolve, stand out, and outperform the market. Hence, leaders could become more important than ever, raising their own digital literacy, investing heavily in people development, and demonstrating the kind of extraordinary leadership required in an ever-evolving landscape. In many ways, the real opportunity is being ready to stand up for the longer term with this investment in people, going against a strong near-term focused, pro-AI trend that prioritizes immediate profits over humanity and future business sustainability.

The emphasis on machines, processes, and structures plays into, and perhaps emanates from, the dominant masculine culture in many firms. In contrast, the pursuit of a unique, distinctive, people-centered brand and culture means there could be a greater need for leading from the feminine, with an emphasis on traits such as empathy, social awareness, sensitivity, and collaborative working. Feminine might be just one word for it, but ultimately it is a perspective that puts people, relationships, and the long-term above efficiency and short-term cost savings.

New Professions and Ethical Frameworks

The technologies coming through will also enable and require new professions. For example, as driverless vehicles get closer to becoming a market reality, we may see the rise of the "autonomous ethicist"— specialists who attempt to work out the ethics necessary to program autonomous vehicles. This is going to be a social, moral, ethical, political, economic, and—ultimately—legal minefield. Many citizens, and every country, city, region, regulator, insurer, religion, civil rights group, and car manufacturer will want to contribute to the debate. The goal is to try and establish the rules and assumptions that will underpin the decision-making within an autonomous vehicle as it becomes aware that it is about to have an accident.

Should a self-driving vehicle prioritize the safety of its passenger, the pedestrian who stepped in front of it, or the pregnant mother on the pavement beside them? Should it put the interests of the taxi owner over those of the driver? How will it make those choices? Will it use facial recognition to identify individuals, and pull our tax records and other public information to work out what our net worth is to society or what our future contribution might be? How will it assess the contribution of a writer or journalist versus a baker, doctor, or actuary? What if it chooses to run down an irreplaceable hundred-year-old tree instead of a human? In a Hindu village in India, for example, running over a cow to save a passenger might be viewed as the worst possible outcome, and therefore the ethics programmed into the vehicle may prioritize the safety of the sacred animal over that of the human. Our ethicists will have to take account of all these different perspectives in constructing their guidance, and this could vary dramatically even within a country.

The Rise of New Sectors and Markets

Over the next decade, if things follow the "preferred future" that most nations and businesses are pursuing, the global economy could grow from about US$78Tn today to around US$120Tn. More than half of that is likely to come from businesses that have emerged recently or don't yet exist, and over 80% will almost certainly be from products and services we don't have today.

Industries will also change, with technology giving them a lower risk profile. Smart farms might mean fewer crop failures, the IoT could enable smart cities with better hazard prevention, and self-driving cars should theoretically never have accidents. Hence, the notions of self-owning and self-insuring vehicles becomes a possibility. An array of equally dramatic developments across a range of other sectors could have potentially serious implications for insurance. Furthermore, changing lifestyles, potentially lower real-term incomes, and smart tracking technology are all driving growth of the sharing economy and scenarios where ownership is becoming obsolete, and more possessions are shared and not owned by one individual. This goes along with the shrinking value of owning something and instead purchasing access to it. Shared items could come insured as part of the deal, thus negating any need for buying individual policies. The risks might be borne by the users and reflected in the price.

The growing experience economy also creates opportunities. For the developed world and middle classes everywhere, we are at a time in history where experiences are starting to matter more than things—while tricky to insure, these products could take a similar form to trip insurance. Infinitely flexible policies could be designed to protect people against bad dates or wasting their time on a movie they didn't enjoy. The payout could vary from a ticket refund through to the cost of counseling and treatment should the experience be truly traumatizing.

Conclusion—Nurturing Human Qualities

To enable the kinds of shifts discussed here, a company needs to ensure an effective "innovation architecture" that supports a wide range of innovative thought and action across all employees. Key components would include ensuring leadership and management truly understand both the technologies reshaping our world and the associated mindsets that are creating new and disruptive concepts, strategies, business models, products, and services. At the local level, the freedom and capacity to conduct rapid market-facing experiments is critical—as is the need to have people across the organization seeking out and connecting with emerging businesses and sectors and their respective associations. These market-focused conversations are critical to understanding how current and future sectors and opportunities might evolve. The goal is to gain early access to what might become important future revenue streams.

For a company to navigate the decades ahead it needs to see itself as a living, breathing, constantly evolving, and very human organization—designed for and by people. This means a culture that embraces continuous innovation and experimentation on both an incremental and a dramatic scale, and willingness to pursue exponential improvements. Such a journey requires a highly empathetic, trusting, and nurturing relationship with employees where technology is seen as a means of allowing them the time to be creative, innovative, experimental, and customer-centric. In parallel, it means being seen to be supportive of those whose jobs are displaced. In short, it means committing to a very human future.

- *How do we go about helping the whole of society understand the fundamental shifts that are shaping our collective futures?*
- *How might the future responsibilities of the firm evolve in relation to the needs of society?*
- *How might we as humans and societies cope with a rapid transition to a post-jobs future?*

This chapter is based on an interview given to Il Bollettino.

What Will Our Children Do? 20 Jobs of the Future

Rohit Talwar, Steve Wells, Alexandra Whittington, Helena Calle, and April Koury

What kinds of jobs might those currently in school or higher education be doing when they enter the world of work?

The Shape of Jobs to Come

Back in January 2010 we wrote a report for UK government on *The Shape of Jobs to Come*. The study highlighted new jobs that might emerge in the global economy by 2030 as a result of exponential developments and breakthroughs in science and technology. Many of those are now real jobs and the rest are still likely to materialize. As an update on those ideas, our recent books *The Future of Business*, *Beyond Genuine Stupidity—Ensuring AI Serves Humanity* and *The Future Reinvented—Reimagining Life, Society, and Business* discuss a whole range of new industries and professions that might emerge as a result of these exponential advances. Presented below are a selection of 20 new jobs that we think could rise to the fore in the coming decade.

New Jobs and New Business Sectors

The exponential pace of advancement in science and technology is going to enable dramatic changes in society. Advances in fields such as artificial intelligence (AI), robotics, autonomous vehicles, blockchain, human enhancement, and hyperconnectivity will help transform industries, enable the birth of new sectors, and lead to a whole new set of professions and jobs. These new professions could draw on multiple underlying disciplines. Here are some examples:

Lifestyle Services

1. *Life Manager for the Techno-Bewildered*—Those who struggle with technology and get left behind in the new world order might find themselves placed under the mentorship of new-age social workers. These Life Managers would supervise our every decision, guide us on how to navigate the day-to-day of a tech-centric world, and help ensure we use our finances or guaranteed basic incomes in a sustainable manner.

2. *Robo-Nanny*—Replacing the human nanny or au pair, future robotic caregivers could become a constant companion to our children at every stage of their development. Every facet of a Robo-Nanny's character could be selected and tweaked by parents—emotional intelligence, values, ethics, levels of optimism, and even how the bot responds to difficult situations such as the passing of a grandparent. The bot could also be programmed to introduce new learning topics, languages, and life skills as required.

3. *Sexual Compatibility Consultant*—The risk of choosing an inappropriate partner and then having the "wrong" child could see the rise of compatibility specialists. These experts would use AI algorithms to assess everything from IQ and EQ to genetic makeup and family medical history to try and ensure we find the right mating partner.

4. *Longevity Relationship Counselors*—With humans expected to live 120 years plus and technology continuing to blur the line between robot and human, new types of marriage and relation-ship counselors may emerge. These lifelong counselors will help coach and guide individuals and their many partners across all

stages and types of relationships, from traditional monogamy to polyamory and even human-robot or human-VR intermingling.

5. *End of Life Planner / Death Strategist*—As lifespans are extended for those who can afford it, deciding when to die becomes a difficult decision. Our choices will need to factor in emotional, healthcare, familial, economic, and tax planning criteria when making the decisions. This will give rise to a new death management profession—part GP, part financial advisor, part family therapist, and part grief counselor.

6. *Urban Foraging Educators*—In the coming decade and beyond, food scarcity may force more of the world's people to forage for healthy food. In cities, where most of the population will be concentrated, urban foraging education may become a matter of survival. There may be a future demand for experts to train the public in identifying poisonous plants, edible weeds, and wild fruits or vegetables so that the population may survive future food shortages. Schools, governments, and private educational providers may seek to hire experts in urban foraging. Future foraging professionals could become as beloved (and marketable) as the celebrity chefs of today.

Enhancement Specialists

7. *Memory Adaptation Specialists*—A memory specialist may help us modify our memories and reduce mental health issues. People would be able to erase traumatic memories and replace them with positive ones. The process might be conducted by a specialist with training in psychotherapy and neuroscience. Modifying our memories could have a major impact on our personality. The memory specialist would help you choose the traumatic events you need to erase. The replacement procedure would be done after a series of introspective consultations. A wide catalog of pleasant memories would be available for your selection. People would choose what they want to remember.

8. *Human Enhancement Technician*—As a society, we are starting to augment the human body with chemical, genetic, electronic, and physical enhancements. Body shops will appear on the high street where appropriately trained technicians will be able to perform these upgrades—administering nootropic drugs, genetic modifications, 3D printed limbs, and electronic brain stimulation.

9. *Cryogenics Concierge*—As more people opt for cryogenic preservation at—or close to—the end of their life, they will need specialist advice. The cryo concierge will provide guidance on different types of cryo procedures, costs, financial planning, the family's rights and responsibilities, what happens when you are regenerated, insurance, and how to manage the death.

New Societal Roles

10. *Independent Fact Checker*—This role already exists to some extent but becomes ever-more essential as concerns grow over the proliferation of fake news, companies exaggerating their marketing claims, and politicians arguing about the veracity of each other's statements. These arbiters of truth will use a swathe of AI systems to check the truth and origin of every claim and fact. Clients will pay them for these services and for a regularly updated assessment of how truthful and accurate their own statements are. Public honesty tables provided by the fact checkers will influence the reputations and fortunes of businesses, politicians, and political parties.

11. *Crypto Detective*—The spread of crypto currencies and initial coin offerings has led to high levels of fraud and concerns over the scale of crypto-based shadow economy transactions. Specialist detectives backed up by AI will be required to unravel crime in the cryptosphere.

12. *Robot Whisperers*—Artificially intelligent robots may comprise a significant part of the future workforce in retail, food service, and hospitality. Companies deploying such robots may require a staff of professional human Robot Whisperers to stand guard whenever

the bots interact with the public. This job would involve behind-the-scenes monitoring of robotic chefs and customer service robots to make sure they don't run over a person's foot or knock over a gas grill or cause other such hazards. The Whisperer would also monitor for undesirable behavioral changes as the robots learn from and adapt to their environment. Although robotic employees could be highly efficient and autonomous, it is possible that unexpected stimuli in the environment could result in accidents or injuries. Robot Whisperers would be a profession geared toward instilling public trust in robot workers.

13. ***Inter-AI Conflict Resolution Specialist***–AIs will increasingly need to collaborate. Our personal intelligent assistant may need to interact with the AIs of our bank, our employers, and all the vendors who serve us. Not all AIs will be born equal or have common goals, so disputes could arise. Human arbitrators may need to intervene to get the best outcome for humanity in these disputes.

14. ***Robo-Cop Coordinator***–With the increasing capability of AI and robotics, policing could be undertaken by automated robotic systems. These might range from humanoid robots capable of interacting directly with the public, through to autonomous road vehicles and drones for surveillance. Human oversight would enable resources to be deployed based on the recommendations made by automated systems given the situation observed. The coordinators would be able to supervise a significant number of policing assets, all of which would be capable of operating 24/7.

15. ***Off-World Governors***–Dreams of inhabiting other planets and subsea colonies could be realized in the next 10-20 years. These new nations will require their own governance systems, economic and monetary frameworks, behavioral norms, decision-making models, laws, ethical standards, and judicial systems. These could vary dramatically from those witnessed on Earth. Hence, they will likely require a very different breed of visionary leaders to envision, run, and continuously evolve these new communities.

16. ***Personal Festival Designer***–For the super wealthy, the next must-have experience could be the creation of your own festival—as

birthday parties are so 2018. Your designer would craft the perfect combination of entertainment, glamping accommodation, gourmet food, tech support services, and on-demand transport using drones and autonomous vehicles.

New Industries–New Professions

17. *Autonomous Vehicle Ethicist*–We will need to establish the guiding principles for decisions made by autonomous vehicles. For example, who or what should the car hit if an accident is inevitable? Depending on where you are in the world the decision will be governed by different ethical and religious considerations, societal norms, and even economic factors.

18. *Synthetic Sommelier*–The rise in the use of synthetic food products could drive the emergence of experts on all aspects of edible synthetics, lab grown meat, and 3D printed foodstuffs. These professionals would be excellent at developing the perfect synth meal for any occasion. They can tell you all the differences in smell, taste, and texture between the synth food and its real, authentic counterpart.

19. *Chief Augmentation Officer (CAO)*–Within a decade, an increasing number of staff members could be seeking bodily augmentations that render them close to superhuman cyborgs. These humans 2.0 may need to have different management, working conditions, and workplace rights—all designed and overseen by the CAO.

20. *Space Junk Removal Supervisor*–Near Earth orbit is increasingly congested by the remnants of old space missions, obsolete satellites, and the results of accidental collisions and losses. At the same time, the space sector is expected to explode—encompassing everything from asteroid mining and space tourism to the establishment of off-world colonies. In response, dependent upon the type of junk being targeted, different fleets of specialized space craft would be controlled, deployed, and coordinated by Space Junk Removal Supervisors based at contractors' ground stations. The experience

in low Earth orbit will drive new policies, agreements, and procedures to prevent a similar issue developing around the Moon and Mars.

Are We Ready for Tomorrow's Sectors and Jobs?

When viewed collectively, these jobs may feel too big a stretch for the imagination. However, in every case, we can see relevant developments happening in society and in the underlying fields of science and technology. These suggest that most if not all of these jobs will become a reality in the coming decades. Are our schooling and higher education systems prepared?

- *What are the implications for societal systems and structures that these new potential jobs present?*
- *What are the issues for the existing workforce in a world characterized by radical changes to the workplace?*
- *What are the foundation skills required for a world of new jobs and how should they be taught and learned?*

A version of this chapter was originally published in Empowered Business Magazine under the title "What Will Our Children Do? Jobs of the Future."

Five Business Shifts that Will Put Learning at the Heart of the Agenda

Rohit Talwar and Helena Calle

How can we embrace the strategic importance of learning and development?

Learning, Survival, and Growth

In our recent book *The Future Reinvented—Reimagining Life, Society, and Business*, we argued that, in the face of seemingly unprecedented change across society, learning at every level is central to survival and growth. Here we explore five underlying forces at play that are placing learning and development (L&D) at the heart of tomorrow's organizations.

A Faster Planet—The world is moving and changing at a breakneck pace. Organizations are challenged to make sense of today while keeping an eye on the horizon for the next wave of transformative developments. For leaders, it is increasingly apparent that survival depends on the ability to make sense of change, unlearn what no longer serves, and acquire new knowledge and insights.

Living the Future—Societal shifts, disruptive thinking, and game-changing technologies are shortening the gap between concept emergence and translation into a physical reality. Hence, the growing emphasis on acting faster on insights and reducing the time to "sell" a change internally—because people can see for themselves why it's needed. The implication is that everyone needs to learn to understand how to scan and evaluate signals of impending change around them and on the horizon. From changing customer requirements to futures videos, all provide powerful learning about tomorrow.

Digital Mindsets—Entities are being redesigned around data flows and adopting increasingly digital mindsets—using data to underpin decision-making. While intuition, assumptions, and creativity are important, there's growing emphasis on fact and results-based decision-making. Adopting more systematic problem solving using the scientific method requires a different training approach. Individuals must learn how to approach data, make evidence-based decisions, and draw conclusions using repeatable methods. They also need to learn to make decisions when the data is imperfect or unavailable.

New World Literacy—A wide range of exponentially evolving technologies like artificial intelligence (AI) and blockchain are creeping into workplaces, enabling radically different ways of thinking about how things work and how to achieve outcomes. For example, driverless cars will overturn long held assumptions regarding insurance and vehicle ownership. Hence, a key challenge is to accelerate the speed at which leaders and managers are learning about, and updating themselves on, these disruptive technologies and the ideas they enable.

Smarter Workplaces—Exponentially improving technologies such as AI and robotics are starting to transform workplaces, outperforming humans in many tasks. They are also expanding our capacity to process and interpret vast arrays of data, conduct complex activities with repeatable precision, and automate much of what was exclusively in the human domain. Learning about how to work with these technologies and harness them to unleash our creative talents is central to ensuring organizations see a positive return on their automation investments.

Future performance will undoubtedly be tied to an organization's capacity to learn. The question is whether today's L&D professionals are ready to step into the immense opportunities that are emerging and play a central role in creating tomorrow.

- *Alongside evaluating the cost of L&D, does the organization also look at the costs of having capability gaps?*
- *How can we help individuals take greater responsibility for their own learning journeys?*
- *What capabilities will L&D leaders need in order to help the organization embrace the importance of acquiring new insights and skills?*

A version of this chapter was originally published in Training Journal.

Learning into a Faster Future

Interview with Rohit Talwar

Global futurist Rohit Talwar set minds racing and Twitter buzzing with his captivating keynote speech at the January 2018 Learning Technologies Conference in London. We caught up with him to find out more about his thoughts on the emerging future and how we can prepare the learning and development (L&D) function for the immense opportunities that he believes lie ahead.

Please give us an overview of your recent keynote at Learning Technologies.

The title of my keynote was Human Futures and Emerging Technologies—How Advances in Science and Technology Could Transform the Ways we Live, Work, and Learn. The presentation drew heavily on our recent book *The Future Reinvented—Reimagining Life, Society, and Business* and a new research program we have started on the future of education and learning. My central premise was that individuals, society, business, and governments will experience more change in the next decade than most people in work have experienced in their lifetimes.

I argued that the key determinant of whether we survive and thrive in this rapidly changing reality will be our capacity to let go of outdated worldviews, thoughts, beliefs, and assumptions and our ability to learn continuously about the technologies, ideas, and ways of thinking that are shaping the decade ahead. In short, there is a tremendous opportunity here for learning and development (L&D) to play a critical role in driving our organizations into the future—if we give ourselves permission to believe that's possible.

I highlighted the transformations taking place in the world of work—powered by a combination of disruptive ideas and exponentially improving technologies such as artificial intelligence (AI), the Internet of Things (IoT), blockchain, and immersive tools like augmented reality (AR) and virtual reality (VR). I explored how they were already being deployed in an L&D context, and where their application could go over time.

I emphasized repeatedly my belief that the key challenge for organizations lies in ensuring human-centric differentiation in the face of successive waves of automation that could make us look more and more like our competitors. For learning and development this more central role for L&D sets up some clear priorities. The first is around envisioning, negotiating, and experimenting with L&D's role in the new order. This in turn needs to be underpinned by regular horizon scanning to understand the forces and factors that could shape the future of our organization and L&D over the next one, three, and four to ten years plus. The goal is to use these future insights to develop scenarios of how our operating environment might play out and then craft strategies for the transformation of L&D's role over the next three years to ensure we are flexible and forward thinking enough to respond to any emerging scenario.

Operationally, a more strategic role for L&D means introducing and pioneering new leadership models that break boundaries and challenge cherished orthodoxies which may be holding the organization back. While the future is not all about technology, we believe L&D should also be encouraging the use of gaming, simulation, interactive video, social media, AR, VR, and other technologies to help us make sense of the emerging, radically different environment and navigate a rapidly changing world. Given the centrality of technology to tomorrow's business, L&D also has the imperative of helping the business think digital and evolve digital mindsets and new world literacy. This includes guiding the use of contextual micro-learning and productivity enhancement support for the digital workplace.

Given the pace of change L&D will also have to accelerate its own learning and experimentation with new approaches through internal and external learning collaborations. Finally, the modern workplace and continuous change have their casualties, and so we envisage a growing role in addressing the mental health challenge and providing lifelong learning support tools for displaced employees. While few in the audience disagreed with these new elements of L&D's role, most felt it was some way off their current organizational positioning.

So how do you think L&D will be using AI in five years' time?

Our business systems will generate vast amounts of data about every aspect of an employee's performance. This will drive smart contextual learning that provides input as required through a range of formats such as video instruction. Learning management systems will get smarter and integrate with our personal devices to develop a more holistic picture of what we are learning—although this could be seen as highly intrusive. Simulations and gaming experiences will get more sophisticated in the way they tailor the individual's path through a learning experience. Finally, our personal devices will become our coach, therapist, and learning mentor—bringing in the tools and resources we need where and when we need them. This might range from coaching us on alternative negotiating tactics during a customer call to compiling briefing videos to watch on the way to a client meeting.

You published a series of blogs back in January about predictions for 2018 and beyond—one of them was the wonderfully titled *Artificial Intelligence vs Genuine Stupidity*. Tell us more about this.

This was based on another one of our recent books *Beyond Genuine Stupidity—Ensuring AI Serves Humanity*. We believe that AI will have a transformative effect and we can anticipate the consequences from job losses to mental health issues and rising social anxiety. We argue that businesses and governments need to be thinking ahead and preparing for a range of possible scenarios—not just hoping the issue will go away.

Another of the posts was around the importance of stress management through health checks, mindfulness, sleep advice etc. Do you think tech can play a part here too?
At one level, the technology can play a powerful preventative role with apps that monitor our health, undertake continuous monitoring of our vital signs, guide our meditations, and even teach us how to sleep. However, for many, the cause of their health issues, stress, and sleep loss might be that they are already spending too long behind—and in service of—the screen. Here it seems unlikely that more technology will be the most appropriate answer.

A version of this chapter was originally published in Training Journal under the title "TJ talks to Fast Future's CEO Rohit Talwar About the Future of L&D and his Keynote at Learning Technologies."

Five Possible Uses of Big Data in Future Learning Solutions

Rohit Talwar and Helena Calle

How might big data feature in developing and delivering learning solutions?

The use of big data to improve the learning process offers immense future opportunities. Here we explore five powerful emerging and potential applications.

Learning Effectiveness

While some learning organizations are struggling to find the educational potential of big data, the pioneering AltSchool project is already doing student data trials. AltSchool collects information about several aspects of the teaching/learning process, including the impact of classroom resources, attention spans, and academic performance. The goal is to provide insights to improve teaching and learning effectiveness.

Dynamic Learning System

The system would have big data analytics driving daily provision of ultra-personalized bite-size learning. The artificial intelligence (AI) system would scan the web, filtering on the individual's current tasks, recent performance, preferred learning style, and immediate learning goals. Focusing on the most relevant text, voice, and video content, the system could present key information as short learning videos to the student on a daily basis.

Customized Degree Programs

Students would personalize their degree using course modules that best fit their learning styles. An initial diagnostic test collects data about individual learning styles, and information on response to visual cues, attention span, and memory capacity. Worldwide big data searches of university offerings and free public courses would identify best fit content, and then the student, tutor, and system work together to select the module mix that best meets the course requirements. For example, the system might select five out of more than 200 available Byzantine history modules that best meet the student's learning needs. The student selects a module and negotiates with their university tutor to ensure it fits the degree requirements. The process allows students to design their own route toward achieving personalized learning goals.

Continuous Feedback on Learner Performance

Currently, post-completion marks, grades, and comments are one of the few systems we have to inform learners about their performance. These typically focus mainly on outcomes rather than how the learner competed the task. Big data analytics could enable a shift to providing continuous personalized insights. For example, evaluating how specific teaching styles impact a student's performance, monitoring the strategies used to gather and structure research data, and evaluating steps taken to solve a problem. The system could collect data about the student's actions and behaviors in every stage of the learning process. The data would be compared and analyzed continuously against a database of information on how others have completed similar tasks to make accurate recommendations to improve student performance.

Collaborative and Dynamic Curricula

Government education departments often struggle to develop up-to-date curricula to guide schools accurately on the future needs of business and society for which students should be prepared. Instead, citizens and businesses could be given more say on what schools teach. Through periodic surveys and continuous input, the system could collect societal views on what students should learn—from essential life skills to knowledge on how society is changing. Using AI tools to evaluate the resulting big data stores of public opinion, schools could receive regular and on-demand updates of what students should be learning about.

These are only five examples of the potential future uses of big data and AI in education. The potential clearly exists to use accumulated insights to transform learning, the challenge is to select a few key opportunities with which to start testing the possibilities.

- *What other potential uses of big data could you see adding value in the processes of teaching and learning?*
- *Which technologies could be used to facilitate data collection in the educational context?*
- *How might data analytics inform the managerial decision-making processes in educational organizations?*

A version of this chapter was originally published in Training Journal.

Enhancing Learning Outcomes with Virtual Reality

Rohit Talwar, Steve Wells, Alexandra Whittington, Helena Calle, and April Koury

How might virtual reality impact work and learning in the near future?

Virtual Reality Enters the Learning Space

Virtual reality (VR) is one of the major contemporary technologies being implemented in teaching today with emerging examples that hint at how it could play a role in the future of education. As one of the key experiential technology innovations that has gathered significant attention, current examples of VR in the marketplace include HTC's Vive, Oculus Rift, and SteamVR. As a consumer product, VR is a seemingly magical form of entertainment made possible by emerging technology. The nature of VR changes the way people interact with digital information, including data, knowledge, and alternative scenarios. The many potential benefits of VR in teaching are only beginning to show through.

One of the biggest challenges in education and training is ensuring that whatever is being taught meets the audience's learning needs. In today's complex and fast-paced society, where new discoveries and technologies emerge regularly, learning needs can also change rapidly. In response to these challenges, tools like VR can help educators adapt and refine solutions quickly. This is just the latest instance of innovative consumer electronics tools being employed in teaching—past examples include the internet, social media, mobile phones, and video games.

Emerging Educational Applications

The VR experience allows people to interact with others in a simulated scenario at different and increasingly multi-sensory levels. Educators have found information retention improves when the individual is engaged in such diverse multi-level experiences. Example classroom applications of VR include:

- Visualizing inherently abstract concepts in physics, engineering, mathematics, chemistry, and biology such as exploring geometric shapes in 3D, following signals through the nervous system, and seeing the behavior of physical structures under different loads and environmental conditions.

- Exploring scenarios that are difficult or dangerous to recreate in the classroom, such as the impact of combining hazardous chemicals, the behavior of the heart during a cardiac arrest, and monitoring lava flows and temperatures in an erupting volcano.

- Creating virtual realities that help bring to life aspects of the curricula and learning objectives in a more engaging manner. For example, traveling virtually to a scenario that brings to life the major facts and details of the history of pre-Hispanic cultures or the different conversations and tensions that led to past wars.

- Enabling students with special needs to experiment with different learning strategies that do not rely on passive listening or reading. For example, learners with attention deficit, hyperactivity, and dyslexia could potentially learn more effectively through experimentation in virtual contexts.

The Workplace Opportunity

There are also a range of possible VR applications in the work environment:

- Demonstrating architectural models and testing factors such as human behaviors during emergencies.
- Advanced multi-sensory simulation of complex and dangerous tasks and activities, encompassing surgery, flying a supersonic jet, and fixing a component on the outside of a spacecraft, through to rehearsing combat or disaster rescue scenarios.
- Making abstract data more tangible to help workers understand information more deeply and promote a better decision-making process. The scope and scale of daily choices can be visualized more easily in VR. For example, a 3D map of the likely return on effort invested for different potential customers might make it easier to determine where to focus sales activity.
- In a variety of contexts, people will be able to create different virtual worlds and test alternative strategies, explore possible solutions, and surface unintended consequences. For example, when launching a new product to a new market, the creation and exploration of parallel virtual market entry scenarios would enable employees to evaluate which choice might best fit the current strategy.
- In corporate training, VR could help accelerate the learning process by allowing people to run through multiple real-world scenarios for the application of a skill, for example practicing coaching skills with virtual people that possess different attitudes and personalities. Training can also be done in situ, for example providing a VR overlay to guide a remote maintenance engineer through the removal and repair of an aircraft engine part, when the plane is 10,000 miles from its home base.

Enhancing Human Experience

Virtual reality is also being put to use in ways that can enhance the social, emotional, and mental conditions for humanity in general—an increasingly important priority for education and training in a world where there is a growing fear of technology usurping humans. For example:

- Virtual reality offers the opportunity to bring people together in applications ranging from shared dating experiences and family reunions through to global team meetings and conflict resolution processes. Whether as our avatars or holograms, we can interact and retain a sense of personal contact with people across the globe in these shared experiences.

- Virtual reality can be used to help us face fears or phobias. Improving students' psychological resilience may be one of the more difficult challenges of educating for the future—technology that can simulate sensory experiences in a nonthreatening way might be among the best strategies to build inner strength. In fact, growing levels of anxiety and stress observed in society might be alleviated by virtual social settings, possibly using artificially intelligent VR therapists or confidantes.

- Simulations in VR can be used to increase empathy, appreciate other viewpoints or experiences, and even address mental health problems. For example, schizophrenia patients may gain better control over their reality and their mental state by interacting with a VR program which replicates the phantom voices and images that they hear and see. This may also help others better understand the experience of those with such conditions. In another example, the manufacturer of a pain reliever demonstrated VR simulations of migraine headaches to the family members of migraine sufferers as a way to help caregivers understand the traumatic pain of such headaches. Similar empathy exercises might help people gain insights on what it is like to be disabled, dyslexic, elderly, or chronically ill.

Conclusion—In Virtual Service of Humanity

There are clearly a wide range of potential applications emerging for VR in the education and training context. Indeed, using VR to achieve academic, technical, as well as relational goals is one of the most promising approaches to the future delivery of education and training. Moreover, in a rapidly changing world, perhaps the most valuable potential contribution of VR in education and training will be in helping enhance our capacity for understanding, caring, and empathy. With technology automating many job roles, the best employment opportunities will likely require far more than technical abilities. Qualifications for good jobs are already evolving toward abstract criteria, like cultural fit. This suggests that, in the future of hiring, interpersonal faculties and emotional intelligence could supersede educational credentials, or even work experience. This may be the most beneficial but surprising application of VR in education and training.

- *Which hard to teach topics or ideas could be more easily conveyed with VR?*
- *What are the potential advantages and disadvantages of using VR in the classroom?*
- *How can educators retain the human element in their classes, while embracing technology? How should we feel about children of different ages using VR? Should there be age limits?*

A version of this chapter was originally published in Training Journal under the title "Virtual Reality—Enhancing Learning Outcomes."

PART 5:
Business, Work, and the Workplace

Implementing AI in the Workplace—The Leadership Development Challenge

Rohit Talwar, Steve Wells, and Alexandra Whittington

How can we raise the capabilities of business leaders to operate effectively in an AI-enabled environment?

The AI Leadership Challenge

As artificial intelligence (AI) enters the workplace, it is becoming increasingly clear that business leaders need new skills to rise to the challenges and opportunities presented by this disruptive new technology. Here we explore the nature of the new challenges and some of the key capabilities that might be required to respond effectively in a world where the old rules no longer apply.

Automation, Humans, and Brands

Firstly, let's consider the changing nature of work itself. Right now, task automation is a key area for AI applications. Roles traditionally thought of as requiring a high-level human intellect are now being automated. For example, AI is now undertaking the work of share analysts and fund managers and doing the bulk of the scanning of medical research and past cases to determine the potential causes of a patient's symptoms. Similarly, the legal profession is starting to see disruption through AI: automating searches for legal precedents and case reviews, creating and adapting contracts, predicting litigation outcomes, and organizing workloads.

While AI can boost efficiency, decision makers must be mindful of how this may impact brand identity and user experience—and where it is still critical to maintain human involvement. As similar approaches to smart automation are deployed by competing businesses, there's a risk of us all looking the same, which in turn leads to commoditization. How firms stand out and maintain personality will be a critical consideration; the real pay-off comes from deploying the technology to unleash human potential and take our businesses to the next level— rather than simply automating what we have in order to reduce costs.

Although the technology is potentially complex, the critical success factor for business leaders and managers is to focus on the human dimension. How will staff respond when their jobs are changed drastically or eliminated? How will we mitigate the worries or stress that the introduction of AI may cause? What new skills might employees need? What responsibilities do employers have for those displaced by technology—some analysts predict that 80% of current jobs could disappear within 20 years, and the OECD estimates that for each job created in new firms and sectors, three or more will be eliminated elsewhere.

Defining and Learning into Leadership's New Role

So, what do leaders need to understand and pay attention to as their organization embarks on the AI journey? What training may they need to make the most of the opportunities without ignoring the human factor? And who should lead the implementation of AI within the business?

It may be natural to think that the IT department should be the driving force behind business adoption of AI. However, the increasingly strategic nature of the decisions embedded in the choice to deploy AI may be seen as sitting more in the realm of the COO, CEO, or heads of business units and functions. Importantly, the learning to support these leadership decisions can be drawn from a multitude of different places. Attendance at industry associations, public conferences, and specialist events, can all facilitate learning and networking opportunities, and vendors can share their experience and advice.

Discussions with other organizations who've experimented with AI can allow us to tap into their knowledge and experience. The internet is also a rich source of short videos and explanatory content that can accelerate our understanding of AI and its potential impact on our sector and our customers. Finally, science and technology graduates can intern to bring technical expertise, create a resource to run rapid AI application experiments, and provide fresh perspectives to a firm in exchange for business experience.

By gaining a better understanding of AI and its implications it will be easier to make decisions about how narrowly or how deeply to deploy AI within the business. Today, AI can be used narrowly to automate a single task or apply rule-based thinking to a process or outcome, or it may be used to automate entire functions, e.g. customer service. How deep to take AI will depend on the goals, priorities, resources, and values of the firm and where leaders see the place of humans in service, innovation, and sales.

Driving Transformation

In an increasingly turbulent and uncertain landscape, individuals are naturally becoming increasingly concerned about their own prospects. There is a growing risk that firms will become over-reliant on technology and ignore the value of humans. In this environment, leaders need heightened levels of compassion, emotional intelligence, and social awareness. Honesty about potential workforce impacts is critical here if we want to engage staff in the transformation process. People want to know how they will be assisted through the transition, what will happen to their jobs, and how they will be supported if they are made redundant.

Smart technology will increasingly replace even complex roles; however, it will be some time before it can outperform humans in problem solving, creativity, negotiation, collaborative design, conflict resolution, and crisis response. Digital transformation initiatives typically fail as a result of paying too little attention to the human and cultural aspects of change and their place in the future solution. Hence, we need to think about how to invest in staff to maximize their potential with technology as an enabler, and how to care for those whose roles and departments are being disrupted by AI. Critically we need to focus on how to raise everyone's digital literacy, so they understand the nature of the technology that is bringing about such change in their world and the possibilities it enables.

Training may be necessary to facilitate the transition to working in an AI-centric firm; something akin to cultural or sensitivity training to allow employees to become accustomed to working with, or being managed by, the new technology. HR may have a greater role to play in professional development; for example, a senior manager whose job is being fundamentally disrupted for the first time in their career may need a degree of retraining and emotional support. Hence, soft skill training may become more and more important as leaders and their teams will need to hone skills like sensitivity, creativity, verbal reasoning and communication, empathy, and spontaneity. HR or a new Department of Humanity can facilitate this aspect of personal development to ensure that businesses make the most of the interplay between human and artificial intelligence.

Overall, finding a balance between AI and the human workforce in their organizations will be key for every leader. In order to preserve the human element of your business in an automated climate, what will act as a key differentiator? Careful decisions about which roles and functions to automate should guide AI strategy—a simple "bottom line" approach will compromise the human element and could erode the firm's uniqueness over time. It will also be important to show compassion and support to employees displaced by new technology.

Harnessing AI's Gifts for All Humanity

The gifts from AI to society include smarter decision-making, the capacity to draw new insights from vast arrays of data, the potential for cost-saving replacement of humans, and efficiency-oriented high-volume applications which are simply beyond human capacity to execute in a meaningful time frame, for example scanning literally millions of websites in an information search. However, a sweeping implementation of AI without regard for the impact on employees would be bad internal PR at the least and could actually have devastating consequences in terms of customer appeal and local reputation for a business.

Ultimately the future of work and the future of society are deeply entwined. Our sense of place in society, our worth, our contribution, and our legacy are often predicated around our work. Anything that starts to disrupt that relationship between work and individual identity is going to have far-reaching impacts. On the plus side, humans have proved themselves to be remarkably adaptable. So, while the idea of working side by side with a robot, or being supervised by it, may at first be unsettling, a small step back reminds us that we already work and relate with AI and "smart" machines every day. For example, predictive text is a form of AI software which most smartphone users have adjusted to. When sending emails or texts on devices, or running an internet search, we expect, to some extent, that our intention will be perceived.

The AI companions that will join us in the workforce will be preoccupied with learning about us to try to make our lives better. Just as the predictive text on your phone doesn't (normally) send runaway messages, and the internet search bar sometimes knows you better than you know yourself, we as a society should anticipate AI's helpful (if sometimes at first clunky) role in the workplace over the coming decade.

- *What is your organization doing to support leaders operating in an AI-rich environment?*
- *What leadership issues can you anticipate around the introduction of AI?*
- *What does determining the right human-technology balance mean in practice, and how can we determine what that should look like?*

A version of this chapter was originally published in Training Zone under the title "Leadership development challenge: implementing AI in the workplace."

Blockchain and the New World of Work

Rohit Talwar and Alexandra Whittington

How might blockchain technologies impact the future workplace?

Blockchain and the Future of Work

A new world of work is on the horizon. Specifically, the development of blockchain technology has created new opportunities to rethink how and where we work. How has blockchain impacted the workplace so far, and where is it going in the near future? This chapter explores how blockchain might play a role in the new world of work.

Blockchain is the distributed ledger technology that provides the transaction platform for Bitcoin and other cryptocurrencies. Essentially, blockchain is a financial transaction tracker, but that isn't all it does. Smart contracts are one of the most common examples of blockchain being used for non-currency purposes. A smart contract represents tasks that can be executed without human intervention. An example would be a smart contract for the shipment of tangible goods. New office furniture could be ordered using a smart contract that releases payment via blockchain once the delivery of the furniture is confirmed via Internet of Things (IoT) sensors located within the product itself that verify its physical location. Once the conditions of the contract are met, payment is made instantaneously. The advantage is the automation of many business processes. The disadvantage is the displacement of people who once did most of the jobs to complete the process described above.

Blockchain for Workplace Education and Training

Eventually, blockchain ledgers might replace CVs as the best and most immutable representation of one's professional, educational, and training history. This would prevent people making fraudulent claims and protect against identity theft. For example, as a database of transcripts and credentials, blockchain-based education credits are universal, transparent, and easily verified. Human Resources could make use of such a blockchain to offer company webinars, wellness counseling, and explain employee benefits to new hires, and enable the firm to track who has completed each training module.

Learning about non-traditional subjects could also be managed with blockchain technology. There could be emphasis on numerous areas of learning besides work-related topics, including personal development and mental health. In fact, one type of course that might be offered in a co-working or flexible working environment could involve new employee orientation to the space with safety, environmental, legal, and ethical training related to the job role or guidelines for use of the facility. Proof of training completion would be stored in blockchain for future reference. Already, a company called EchoLink, a training and skill verification start-up, has developed a blockchain token akin to Bitcoin. By applying the blockchain concept to hiring, EchoLink has created a global digital currency designed exclusively for confirming job candidate work history, education, and skills.

Blockchain is a Catalyst for Future Jobs and Industries

As a catalyst for new jobs, blockchain's key capacities make it possible to imagine positive future job roles like food supply chain tracking, counterfeit prevention, and certification of cruelty-free consumer products. For example, blockchain is bringing transparency to the food industry with distributed ledgers that verify everywhere a piece of produce has traveled along its journey to the market. Is it possible that eventually it will be someone's job to track grocery orders on the blockchain, ensuring that food hasn't been tampered with or traveled through ethically dubious routes? As the blockchain industries grow, they will extend their reach into the business community. The industrious city of Berlin is home to a location called Full Node, a new co-working space devoted exclusively to blockchain experimentation, community education events, and hackathons. Full Node is one example of the emerging need for workspaces dedicated to creating clusters of blockchain innovation and raising public awareness for blockchain technology.

Blockchain is Essential to Emerging Future Business Models

A start-up called Primalbase allows lifetime universal membership to co-working spaces via a sharing economy blockchain model which permits coin owners to experience peer-to-peer workspace arrangements. The model allows for completely automated and anonymized real estate transactions Airbnb-style, but transactions are one hundred percent machine-to-machine. Smart devices using a combination of the Internet of Things (IoT) and artificial intelligence (AI), and blockchain would most likely form the basis of a real-life decentralized autonomous organization (DAO). These entities have no human workers or bosses, just a chain of smart contracts triggering—and being triggered by—one another to achieve digitally-enabled tasks across the organization. Eventually, blockchain could allow for co-working and flexible office space that can automatically invoice and collect tenant fees via pre-agreed conditions enabled with a smart contract.

The future of work rests not just upon blockchain; other exponential technologies like AI and IoT are amplifying the smart objects and systems context that characterizes the workplace of the future. Blockchain may disrupt the future workplace in several ways, having many effects on an office and its inhabitants. Decentralized technologies such as blockchain may in fact create some of the best opportunities for flexible working in the future. The most important point for business leaders to remember is to use technology in the service of humans, and not the other way around.

- *What is the potential of blockchain to automate existing inefficient workplace processes and activities?*
- *How well understood is the disruptive potential of blockchain technology in your organization?*
- *How might blockchain enable a more human focus in the future world of work?*

A version of this chapter was originally published in CEO World Magazine under the title "Facts About Blockchain and the New World of Work: Things You Didn't Know."

AI and SMEs—How Small to Medium Enterprises Can Take Advantage of the Technology

Rohit Talwar and Katharine Barnett

How can small to medium enterprises capitalize on the emerging potential of artificial intelligence?

Artificial Intelligence

The increasing power of artificial intelligence (AI) and the subsequent decrease in the associated costs of using it has resulted in many highly useful potential applications of the technology for small to medium enterprises (SMEs). There is now an opportunity for SMEs to use the various applications to maximize their business potential. Here we offer some examples of the applications and strategies SMEs can adopt to take advantage of AI's potential.

Applications

We have reached a stage in its evolution where AI has many potential applications that an SME can harness. For example, across almost every sector customer service can be improved, time management systems introduced, marketing strategies enhanced, and tasks automated. In the front line, AI-powered chatbots can function as highly skilled customer service assistants. Using AI and big data analytics the chatbot will have a wealth of information to draw on from past inter-actions to deliver answers and provide support to your customer base. As these bots can effectively analyze and codify all past interactions between your staff and your client base, they will be able to know your customers better than you know them.

As AI grows in power and comes down in price it can be used to enhance existing services at low cost. For example, AI processing can be applied to your social media platforms to create highly sophisticated marketing strategies. An AI program can analyze interactions on social media, in newsletters, and blog posts to assess the most influ-ential markers; what headlines work best, what key trigger words work well, what times of day people are interacting and responding—all this information can be captured. Thereafter it can be used to deliver differentiated and bespoke marketing campaigns. Each interaction can be unique to the recipient—using language and formats they are most likely to respond well to.

SMEs are in a key position to benefit from the time saving and time management opportunities that AI can offer. For example, Google has already applied AI to generate inbox replies, as well as internal management platforms that promise to consistently return your inbox to zero. These applications can cut down on time-consuming but simple administrative tasks allowing people the freedom to develop more in-depth customer relationships.

Equally, AI can be taken further to assist or even replace entire jobs; routine tasks can be automated by an AI. A key area that is continuing to see AI automation is the legal sector; firms of all sizes are automat-ing the everyday work of employees such as paralegals. Automating an aspect of your business can have multiple benefits; it can introduce consistency to the task while cutting costs and saving time—freeing up people and financial resources to devote to growing your business.

Many AI applications are available as open source, or online as a software as a service (SaaS) solution. As open source is built from the ground up it can be customized to your individual business's needs. It allows an application to be built without any unnecessary extra features, whereas SaaS sees software already built to be used for a specific purpose, ready for companies to purchase. Buying software to run a service, such as an AI-powered marketing campaign, is low cost and easy to use. It can especially benefit SMEs who may be looking to make a small investment with a relatively high value return.

Strategies for Uptake

While there is remarkable transformative potential, SMEs must establish internal processes to assess what technologies to adopt and how to implement them. Not every technology will be appropriate for every business. Hence, SMEs need to spend time deciding where to direct resources in order to avoid investment being wasted in unnecessary technologies. Importantly, time must be spent researching your industry sector and where the opportunities might lie. This can be through talking to customers, suppliers, and colleagues, and by opening up dialogue with industry networks, and even past business partners and collaborators. Encourage your IT department to network in person and online to stay abreast of what other similar departments are doing. An industry association can be a great resource for such networking opportunities, as well as providing information on developments in your industry.

Additional investment may be appropriate for some; if your business sees the opportunity and has the bandwidth, perhaps an AI specialist could be brought in to give a perspective on potential applications.

There are some key questions to consider when deciding where and how to deploy artificial intelligence:

- *How deep to take it?* AI can have many levels of impact. It can be used narrowly for simple rule-based applications, such as processing routine data. Equally, it can be used in a narrow customer-facing application such as running a marketing campaign. For other businesses, a broader approach can have benefit, such as using AI across much of the HR department to automate a wide range of HR processes and internal services. How deep to take AI applications will depend on comfort with the technology and your desired outcomes.

- *What would success look like?* This is an especially pertinent question for SMEs, who should be conscious of not getting overwhelmed by the potential applications. Having a realistic picture as to the desired outcomes for your AI application will help you decide what to use and how to use it.
- *Who should lead?* Depending on your team composition, the responsibility could lie with the CEO, COO, or heads of department for leading the way in incorporating AI into your business.

AI has great potential to improve many aspects of SME performance, and can be used very narrowly for a single campaign, or in a wider application to take over a whole task, even a whole department. Hence, given the pace of AI technology development, SMEs have a wide variety of possibilities before them; deciding where to invest in and how deep to take the technology are critical choices in establishing how to maximize the benefits.

A version of this chapter was originally published in Bytestart under the title "Embracing Technological Opportunities—How SMEs Can Adopt New Technologies Without Being Overtaken by Them."

Humans and Work in the Digital Era—The Next 20 Years

Rohit Talwar, Steve Wells, and Alexandra Whittington

Transformative technological changes are reshaping our organizations; what could this mean for the future of work?

Decentralizing Technologies and the Future of Organization Design

We are often asked "what is the future of organizations?" Over the next 15-20 years, organizational structure and the nature of work as we know it seem likely to undergo drastic changes. Technology is already decentralizing, and automating business and external boundaries are becoming more fluid as we integrate into wider collaborative ecosystems. As a result, the scope and focus of organizations will evolve on a continuous basis. In the face of such shifts, this chapter intends to shed some light on the possibilities of what organizations of the future might look like and how we will work.

There is already incredible variation in the structure of workplaces and in how work gets done. We expect and hope for such diversity to be amplified in the next 20 years rather than reduced into a single scenario of the "future of work." Of course, we expect technology, and in particular artificial intelligence (AI) and blockchain, to penetrate every sector and have a major influence on the shape of things to come.

How might these emerging and disruptive technologies impact our notions of everyday work? If current exponential rates of technological progress continue, in 20 years we could have computing capabilities anywhere from 500 to 10,000 times more powerful than we have today. This could be replicated across every domain of information technology, encompassing fields such as artificial intelligence (AI), machine learning, robotics, drones, big data stores, quantum computing, hyperconnectivity, cloud computing, sensor devices, the Internet of Things (IoT), 3D/4D printing, and augmented and virtual reality.

A combination of these exponential technologies, new business thinking, evolving societal expectations, and economic shifts could result in an ever-broadening spectrum of organizational models. At one end will be those fully automated decentralized autonomous organizations (DAOs) with no employees—many already exist—such as Teambrella the insurance company in the Netherlands. At the other extreme will be those firms that pride themselves on doing their work the way it has always been done. From handcrafted furniture artisans to super secretive personal law firms serving ultra-wealthy individuals, and the millions of new jobs that will hopefully emerge in the creative arts, their work will we be done much as it is today and as it was 20 years ago.

In the middle of the spectrum, we'll see a lot of entities using technology in three key ways: i) to automate away human roles; ii) to augment specialist roles to free up humans from the robotic parts of their work; and iii) to do information manipulation at a scale and speed which humans could never do. A lot of organizations will realize that to keep their firm differentiated will require the creative spark of humans and the personal touch. While a robot could serve me and manage my account and AI could conduct the entire bidding, contract, and delivery process for a $50 million building project, some clients may simply prefer dealing with humans.

Personal Technology, Collaboration, and Communication

As the boundary between technology and the human body starts to blur, what might the impacts be on the way we interact with our environment? Some hope that we will see exponential advances on the already impressive current progress in brain computer interfaces and wireless brain-to-brain communication. Almost certainly, voice and gesture will have eliminated the bulk of interactions with everything from our refrigerator and vacuum cleaner to whatever replaces the computer and smartphone in 20 years' time.

Our devices could become way smarter, monitoring everything from our breathing, oxygen intake, and heart rate through to walking speed, voice patterns, and fluid consumption. They will use the data to determine or anticipate our moods, needs, and desires, and act accordingly to manage the world around us. Simply think of a colleague we want to talk to and our AI will be able to determine who it is and connect us as a result of comparing current and historic data on our brainwaves and bodily functions.

If we get to thought transfer, all sorts of new opportunities emerge. Instant chat really does become instant, emails get replaced by thought exchange, and lies might become a thing of the past. There are also challenges. How will we manage the constant flow of information bombarding us all the time? Imagine all your emails being opened in front of you to be read the moment they arrive, all the time. How will we hide our personal thoughts, how will we prioritize the information coming in, how will we keep conversations private? We might need AI implants in our brain to manage all of this on our behalf and act as a privacy guardian and brain concierge serving up what we need when we need it.

Future Workplace and Project Communications

Projects are becoming the lifeblood of organizations, but our methods of team communication still leave a lot to be desired. If we look ahead 20 years, will we still be discussing projects in never-ending email threads? In a smart tech-enabled scenario, projects would be managed very differently. Manager AIs would draw on past project records to determine how to structure and coordinate similar new work tasks. Most routine work would be automated in the type of workplace environments we've imagined here and so the work the humans do will increasingly be project-focused.

The email scourge is generally driven by poor communication, misunderstood requirements, competing priorities on our time, and unrealistic deadlines. Smart project management systems could help eliminate these issues. Brain-to-brain communication will also help, and the biggest contributors to the death of email will be far better training in communication, collaboration, project working, dispute resolution, problem solving, scenario thinking, and accelerated learning.

Slack, Facebook Workplace, Microsoft Teams and G Suite, and other such work communication tools will evolve and become far more ubiquitous in the next decade—covering ever-larger parts of the work we do. As humans get replaced by machines for a lot of traditional activity they are likely to shift their focus to more creative tasks. In response, newer group productivity tools will also start to emerge that have far more seamless connectivity between constantly changing business applications, workflow management, and the communications requirements of the team. The less human involvement in the flow of routine activity, the more the technology will enable smooth interconnection between systems and an accelerated flow of routine work.

Social Media and Networks

As millennials enter the workplace and drive adoption of social media tools, how might this impact our ways of working? Our social media tools are becoming increasingly vital for work tasks from conference calling and team coordination to customer communications and complaint handling. The importance of this functionality is likely to grow and then disappear into the background as the social part of social media simply becomes part of how we work—with AI doing more of the social connection on our behalf. As part of the work environments mentioned above, we'll see ever-greater integration of existing and customizable social media tools.

As the technology gets smarter, for individuals, the boundaries will disappear between email, text, voice, work social media, private social media, and direct brain drops—everything will become a curated flow of information managed by a personal AI. In this world, the distinction between LinkedIn, Facebook, YouTube, Slack, and every other platform will evaporate—they all just become inputs to your inbox. We are currently obsessed by these brands, but 95-99% of tech ventures fail eventually, so we can expect casualties even among the current masters of the digital universe. The brands may die but the functionality and multimedia user experience will live on.

To take a radical leap into the future, automated sharing and resource allocation—from staplers to massive display screens—could introduce a new social ecosystem that enhances new behaviors and skills around collaboration, sense-making, curiosity, scenario thinking, and work. The organization could also provide support to the local entrepreneurial ecosystem in terms of employment, training, start-up support, and start-up pitching. There could be incubator facilities for internal and external ventures alike. Some of the larger organizations of the future might see it as part of their civic remit to provide multi-purpose facilities for yet to be determined internal uses and to support "grand challenge" societal redesign projects—for example, experiments in housing courtrooms, doctors' surgeries, social centers, and libraries in the evenings, at weekends, and during holidays.

The End of Email?

Will we finally wean ourselves off email addiction? A lot of the developments described here will chip away at the current role of the email. However, its total demise will be a long time coming. Security requirements, personal comfort, inertia, and a lack of trust in the new technology platforms in some quarters will ensure that email lives on for at least another 5-10 years—even if the way in which it presents to us changes dramatically over that time frame.

The Possible Shapes of the Next Future

The next logical question is, what comes after email, Slack, and Facebook? We think there are a combination of evolutionary and unexpected developments in how we work which could become significant in the next five to ten years. At the core is the notion that as technology frees us from the routine, there will be a growing focus on value creation through collaboration and co-creation with internal external partners, which could see a shift toward more "walk and talk" meetings and less fixed appointments.

Technology and AI will undoubtedly sit at the heart of the next wave of work design, with a growing reliance on life automation tools—multi-app personal AI assistants managing our workday. These will be coupled with the digital twins performing the bulk of our routine tasks. Our AIs are increasingly likely to be performing tasks such as document review and triaging all our inboxes to extract salient information and send auto-responses. As we do our work and take on new tasks, we can expect to see growing use of context-sensitive, in-task, and on-demand personalized training. Such continuous monitoring of the work people do should allow us to spot productivity problems and poor approaches to tasks. The systems will evaluate how we are doing the job and then draw on vast global databases of information on others doing similar tasks from systems like Office 365 to provide instant written, verbal, and video guidance on how to do each task more efficiently and effectively to improve our performance.

In the background, we could see growing use of context-aware AI voice assistants responding to requests and proactively listening to conversations. Such tools would bring relevant information into view on demand or on an anticipatory basis, mute participants automatically, record and transcribe the discussion, and summarize the outcomes. As these tools will have a better and constantly updated understanding of what each of us knows, they could highlight and research new terms and concepts that are mentioned in the discussion and share the findings with us discretely—perhaps overlaying the information on our contact lens displays.

The rise of new sectors and the new possibilities enabled by technology could see exponential growth in terms of the number of roles focused on humans and AI working together to extract and act on insights from vast data arrays. The greater the reliance we place on technology, the faster core work will get done, which could potentially create pressure and tension points wherever humans interact with the machines and decisions are required to enable the flow of work to continue. Our capacity to keep pace with the speed of business is already being challenged and this is likely to be exacerbated as AI enters the scene. Making our work lives more sustainable will require a radical rethinking of priorities and a cultural commitment to make our workplaces more human. Whatever happens, we are likely to see a growing need for regular disconnection and retreat in oases of calm and reflection within the workplace.

Preparing for Multiple Possible Futures of Work

No one can accurately predict where the future of work will take us in the next few decades, but the developments taking place today and the ideas emerging from research labs creating the next waves of technology give us some pointers around what our systems might do. The technology may allow us to operate seamlessly around the globe, provide genuinely consistent levels of service 24/7/365, and become far better at predicting issues and solving problems. One thing is certain: we will be learning constantly, and smart systems will be a key resource. In parallel we need to be focusing our efforts on enhancing human capabilities to help us perform in whatever jobs and roles we might be undertaking. From raising digital literacy to enhancing our communication and collaboration skills, continuous learning will be the essential lifeforce for individuals and organizations alike.

- *What are the value-added parts of work we can see human workers focusing on in the future?*
- *What major changes to the structure of businesses are you already noticing and what other changes would you expect to see in the future?*
- *How is your organization addressing the requirement for enhanced future workplace communications and collaboration?*

This chapter is based on an interview given to Forbes India.

Workplace 2040

Rohit Talwar, Steve Wells, and Alexandra Whittington

How might our workplaces and working environments evolve over the next 20 years?

A Healthy Workplace

A healthy workplace makes good use of the latest insights on human behaviors, wellness, and achieving sustainable performance, and deploys the cutting-edge work tools of the times. A wide array of ever-more powerful technologies is becoming part of the core design of organizations—from artificial intelligence (AI) to 3D printing, we now assume they will be part of the fabric of work and the workplace. So, what might these factors mean for the different possible futures of the workplace?

The Boundaries Between Us and Our Devices

The workplace of the future could potentially manifest many of the technological possibilities being developed today. Hence, there are a range of views about how the boundaries between us and our devices might play out in a world of super computing power, particularly in the world of work. Many future visions of work depict an entirely evolved workplace with smart buildings, natural spaces, and advanced architectural elements.

One perspective is that computing will disappear into our environment, and we will command everything by voice, gesture, and thought control. We won't know where the images we are seeing are being projected from and we won't know if the computing is being done by the table, the walls, or the photo frame on the desk. Computing in this scenario becomes ubiquitous, all-pervasive, and highly intelligent. It would be managed by our personal AI assistant to deliver what we want, when we need it, and will continually learn from and adapt to our behaviors and needs.

Another view is that most of what happens will be done in the cloud and then we'll have small chip inserts that provide the local functionality, image projection, voice interface, and connection to the god-like system in the cloud. In many future of work scenarios, the notion is that information will be distributed and managed over the cloud via super secure intelligent blockchains. The whole environment we operate in is likely to be supervised by multiple layers of AI from our personal assistant through to the all-powerful, all-seeing global AIs that manage everything, protect against misuse of our data, and are on the constant lookout for other AIs displaying rogue behaviors.

AI and the Built Environment

In general, the coming wave of AI in business and society could impact the future design, use, and management of buildings in dramatic ways. Key design features, including construction, security, monitoring, and maintenance, could become coordinated by highly automated AI neural networks.

Will the future workspace be a central hub containing key people and activities that all parts of the organization need to tap into, for example advanced meeting facilities, resource libraries, perhaps a foresight center? In these tech-centric work scenarios, how much space might we need for these core functions? With the rise of artificial intelligence, some parts of the organization might run on algorithms alone with literally no human staff. Back office functions could be a prime focus for such an approach. For example, there could be deep automation of HR roles—particularly the management and execution of the recruitment process. Similarly, smart contracts might replace most manual contract creation and administration tasks (e.g. invoice payment), thus reducing the requirement for staff in such roles.

With so many viable visions of the future workplace in the social imagination, how do we plan and rehearse the future effectively? Rather than predict the way future offices will look or feel, let's look at two different time horizons—five to ten and ten to twenty years hence—to examine how the futures could play out.

The Next Ten Years

Cybersecurity—How might our cybersecurity challenges evolve as work becomes increasingly automated? Cybersecurity risks will continue to grow as our reliance on technology deepens ever further. Integrating all our input streams into a single flow has huge elegance and efficiency advantages—it also makes us far more susceptible to be rendered cut off from the digital world by cyberattacks. Despite the ever-growing investment in cybersecurity protection, the hackers and cyberattackers will always be ahead of us because they can move faster, don't care about failure, and are super clear on their goals—which can't always be said about those they are attacking.

Future buildings and workspaces may need to place the need for a constantly evolving cybersecurity infrastructure at the heart of the design process and every aspect of the design of smart environments will need to be parsed through a cybersecurity filter before being approved. Architects working with AI experts, Internet of Things (IoT) specialists, and white-hat hackers might become an increasingly common design team model.

Artificial intelligence, Augmented Reality, Virtual Reality, and Tomorrow's Workplace—Our expectation is that AI will be embedded in every aspect of our world—it already governs domains such as internet searches, smartphone applications, navigation systems, automated share trading, airline autopilots, and mortgage and loan processing. Augmented and virtual reality will play a part but will only go truly mainstream when the devices become unobtrusive and the applications become faster and cheaper to develop. Virtual reality/ augmented reality might be built into the environment of certain spaces as an educational/collaboration resource. Walking VR tours might help with orientation, creativity, and relaxation—helping people explore labs, discovery processes, and nature trails from an enhanced VR space in the building.

A Living Building–The future workspace could become a "living building" with flexibility at its core. We don't know all the intended uses or how they might evolve. Today we might need office space and an incubator for new ventures. Tomorrow we might want a freer flow of people through the space with no requirement to group by function or project. We may also want the capacity to mock up physical environments for the projects we are working on—from a retail street store to a classroom of the future.

Flexibility implies starting to think of buildings as large tents where the activities within can change over time. While we might start with relatively fixed structures, over the longer term we might start to see more use of pop-up 3D printed internal walls and offices, with 3D printing on site of permanent and temporary (project/experiment related) buildings and other facilities. In such an environment IoT sensors and information sources could increasingly be built into the building's components.

Visual Technologies–We can anticipate increasing use of visualization such as on-demand imagery and holography. Facial recognition and smart glasses/contact lenses could, for instance, help us identify everyone we pass in the building and be used as an access control mechanism.

Green Space–Access to nature and natural light within our buildings is likely to remain a design priority. Internal garden and community work areas, use of renewable energy sources (wind, new generation solar paneling), and electric vehicle charging could all be integrated into the design. Integrated vertical farming might maximize use of natural processes and be located in public spaces and atriums in buildings. Vegetation could actually feed the occupiers plus provide a "green" working environment.

Individualized Work Environments—Light, temperature, sound, and imagery all impact how we work. The future workspace could have a strong focus on natural and environmentally friendly workspaces with adaptive personalized light and temperature control, freedom of movement, and spaces for multifunctional collaboration. Individualized flexibility could extend to sit-stand desks, movable walls, and support for seamless integration with remote workers, be that via the desktop or mobile robots.

A combination of IoT connected devices, sensors, and tools could monitor every aspect of employee productivity including keystrokes, time away from the desk, and social interactions. The technology could then intelligently nudge us in personalized ways that encourage productivity based on our performance history. The use of building interior design to evoke certain feelings and enhance moods and creativity, and the use of behavioral insights to motivate the workforce, could provide an important advantage in the new "cobot" normal of humans working alongside intelligent robots.

The Next Ten to Twenty Years

Creativity—In the highly automated future vision of work that many envisage, we could find workers largely doing highly creative tasks with a potentially greater sense of purpose and connection. In this future, the work environment would become the ultimate enabler of cross-boundary working and a place of inspiring beauty. There could be a focus on inclusivity in terms of breaking down boundaries of industries, organizations, and teams, combining digital and physical spaces seamlessly for hassle-free collaboration, creativity, and innovation.

Intelligence in Action—Over this time frame, we can expect even existing technology environments to be retrofitted at relatively low cost to enable on-demand provision of the capabilities required to do whatever the task may be, or to configure the technology solution from a range of plug and play models. Some firms might see the benefit of sharing their IT systems infrastructure with their local community as a support initiative and with their wider business ecosystem to enhance spontaneous collaborations. For larger businesses, conference rooms and support staff could even be shared with guest tenants, which could include technology start-ups, graphic designers, and consulting firms. When not being used as office space, buildings could be used for pop-up adult education courses, retail shops, and civic meetings. This strategy could help build a presence in the community, giving a local feel to a global firm.

Responsivity—We could see growing use of neuro-architecture to build work environments that incorporate biometrics to monitor employee wellbeing, read moods, and respond to people's needs. Entirely person-alized and adaptive control would help maintain people's productivity in the organization by varying lighting, temperature, background music, ambient smells, and digital wallpaper displays according to the changing needs of each individual.

Should current promise be fulfilled, then next generation 4D printed smart materials would allow us to create structures that can change their shape and properties over time—such as space dividers tailored to the needs of each individual. Over this time frame we might also see sufficient advances in genomics to enable us to grow building structures. At the same time, DNA computing could see the fabric of the building storing data and performing computing tasks.

Autonomy—To manage all of these diverse elements, we can envisage the spread of AI-enabled buildings management systems, drone and robotic internal transport, and AI managing energy usage and opti-mizing consumption. Increasingly, autonomous building environments might also incorporate energy harvesting (e.g. piezoelectricity), kinetic energy capture from motion around the building, and intelligent, adaptive, "robotic" infrastructure components such as walls, windows, and cabling infrastructure. Collectively, these developments may remove humans from the facility management equation altogether.

As reality catches up with science fiction, many changes are in store for tomorrow's workplace. Smart, human-centric, sustainable, healthy, autonomous, anticipatory, and even intuitive might be some of the terms which will be used to describe the future of workspaces and buildings. While the technological advances in particular may eliminate many jobs entirely, they will also enable a far more personalized, personable, and conducive work environment. As in every field of development, we have to make sure the trade-offs are always serving the best overall interests of humanity. We can help a maintenance worker retrain and find a new job. It is much harder to help someone recover from the impacts of a stressful or unhealthy workspace.

- *What are the key workplace changes that would contribute to a very human future for you?*
- *What impact will—or might—smarter work tools have on daily work activities in your job or organization?*
- *How can the focus on smarter and healthier workplaces be sustained in the facing of increasing cost and competitive pressures on organizations?*

This chapter is based on an interview given to Forbes India.

PART 6:
Industry Transformation and Disruption

The Future of Energy —Reinvented

Rohit Talwar, Steve Wells, Alexandra Whittington, and Helena Calle

Is your company, organization, or community prepared for a radically reinvented future of energy?

Powering the Planet

Critical to humanity's future survival and wellbeing is the notion of widespread abundant clean energy. However, with energy systems around the world pushed to breaking point in serving current demand, the issue of how we deliver on tomorrow's needs is looming large for players across the energy ecosystem. The problem is exacerbated in summer—the time of year when demands on the world's energy systems typically peak. In many parts of the world this means electrical grids are working overtime to power the cooling and ventilation systems that keep large cities safe from sweltering urban heat. And yet, in other less developed parts of the planet, temperatures will reach deadly levels from which there is no escape, and people will die. Our comfort and survival depend on our ability to continue to power the planet. But because energy is a limited resource, it's not equally distributed.

Radical Energy Scenarios

Most views of the "almost probable certain future" show this situation being addressed slowly over the next five decades—and way too late for many who will perish for lack of a reliable energy supply. But what if we could embrace a fundamental shift in thinking, reset our priorities and investment plans, and set ourselves on a very different path to the future? In our book, *The Future Reinvented – Reimagining Life, Society, and Business* we explored a range of such alternative, surprising, and unexpected future scenarios of how we might change the path to the future across a number of societal domains and industries. In this chapter, we build on those perspectives, combined with new outlooks, visions, and foresight to explore four scenarios for the reinvented future of energy.

The scenarios draw in particular on a workshop on how global societies might be powered in the decades to come, which our team designed and facilitated at the Finland Futures Research Conference in Tampere, Finland in June 2018.

Scenario 1–A Sunlit Solution

This future takes place between 2020 and 2050 and rests on continued progression in the development of organic solar cells and advances in solar panel performance. There is strong focus on peer-to-peer energy distribution systems—cutting out or bypassing the grid could lead to a healthier, renewable, and optimized quality of life. It gives regular people something of value that they can trade or sell to meet their basic needs.

It starts in 2020 with politicians trying to maintain the status quo and resisting the changes being enabled by solar energy. By 2030, the powers that be realize there are more energy producers than consumers. Furthermore, there is enough clean energy to last a lifetime. The pursuit of sustainability becomes a norm across the planet.

By 2040, in this scenario, the claim to ownership of energy could change completely. Each person might be producing their own energy, sharing it with others, and viewing it as something completely renewable and abundant. By 2050, we would see drastic changes in lifestyles. Consider the example life of an Indonesian family with one child; the parents work from home as part of a global network doing professional jobs in a small business. They get to do what they love because abundant energy sources mean they don't have to struggle for basic survival.

One challenge of this future is that almost all natural surfaces are covered in solar panels. This seems at odds with the fact that all local natural and human resources gain more and more value. Natural beauty becomes a rare sight in some places that were once revered for it, such as Indonesia.

Scenario 2—I've Got the Power in Me

This scenario explores a world in 2040 where social values have evolved significantly. The people of this future prioritize open access, trust, and love. Unlike other utopias, we arrive at this wonderful future without a catastrophe. The triggering event is a truly game-changing new energy technology. A personal wearable device is invented to provide personal freedom powered by unlimited energy—capturing and transforming the different forms of energy produced by the body such as motion and heat.

This is a decentralized future where the body can actually produce all the energy needed to run society. There would likely be so much energy available that we wouldn't know what to do with the excess. We could perhaps transform it into technologies that provide shelter, heat, and transport.

On the downside, it is also possible that future uses of abundant energy would be applied for negative purposes. Weapons, pollution, engineered illness, and social control could be some of the darker ramifications of a future where the human body is an energy source itself.

As an example of life in this future, consider Frida who lives in a city in China that stores the energy of the citizens. Not every city has this technology yet, so the city is a prosperous one. The economy is based on energy: producing and selling it. The starting point for the technology was that it was used first to eliminate air pollution.

This was a very popular advancement. The next stage was to develop a complementary technology that enabled the city to store personal energy. In this future, Frida has the freedom to choose what to do with her time because in her daily life she is producing wealth with her own personal energy. She can choose any path she likes or just enjoy the wealth.

Scenario 3—Post-Apocalyptic Networked Nomads

This scenario describes the emergence of a nomad network after an ecological crisis on Earth. It takes place sometime before 2050.

A major climate change induced ecological and civilization crisis has struck the Earth. The rising sea levels destroyed entire cities. The populations that survived live in extreme weather conditions. Society has become nomadic and post-urban.

There is radically less energy consumed per person in this future. Society becomes a series of tribes connected by mobile devices. People have learned the lessons of the disaster, so they are collaborating through their devices and becoming a global mobile community. Energy regulation is based in the values of the nomadic tribes.

Similar to ancient Mongolians, people have robotic horses to move from one place to another, living in tents enabled with solar panels. Cities are not livable, so old buildings and skyscrapers become the platforms for solar panels and storage units.

What does life look like in this scenario? Because of the climate-induced super storms, these tribes cannot practice traditional agriculture. Instead, they have turned to marine agriculture—producing different types of algae that are grown with the use of robots. These farms are not sufficient to support a lifetime's food supply, so the nomads move from one place to another on their robotic horses and wait for new algae to grow in order to come back to harvest their crops.

Scenario 4—An Ikea World

This scenario explores a vision of a smart Scandinavian megacity design colonizing the Earth between 2020 and 2050. Communities have extremely efficient physical infrastructure in terms of housing and residence. However, there are many overlapping activities taking place in the virtual world, which is where the real "community" exists. Mobility has slowed, since self-sufficiency of most buildings reduces the need for transport. Education and work are virtual, urban gardens produce ample food, and waste forms a key energy source. The megacity design encapsulates the self-sufficient zeitgeist of the times.

This future started due to migration problems but thrived thanks to technological innovations. Renewable energy infrastructure, the Internet of Things (IoT), and artificial intelligence gave birth to the optimization of truly intelligent cities and a new network of smart, self-sustaining communities.

Consider the life of the Perez family, who joined a Scandinavian-inspired energy cooperative residential community in Mexico. They are required to adopt a collective mindset, so they commit to becoming more efficient in their energy consumption as tenants of the cooperative. They have everything they need within their comfortable building: ample food from vertical gardens, good neighbors, community entertainment, and a supportive social safety net. Although they live in a tiny apartment, there is plenty of space for kids to explore in the virtual world.

Reinventing Possible Futures

The scenarios deliberately chose to push the boundaries of what our energy future might look like to allow for radical new ideas, environmental disruption, and game-changing innovations. They explore how reinventing the future of energy might unleash new balances of power. How radical are the energy conversations where you live? How are your company, organization, or community preparing for a range of possible futures? If people are operating within narrow paradigms, what can be done to push the boundaries and reinvent the range of possibilities?

From a "whole of humanity" perspective, the tempting proposition here is the combination of adopting new mindsets, using emerging clean energy generation and distribution technologies, and setting new community priorities. Clearly, there are always risks of political and energy sector inaction, with society sinking into a dystopian and chaotic unraveling. For the less optimistic, this may seem like the most likely outcome in some of the scenarios. However, the hope is that the powerful combination of new mindsets, breakthrough technologies, and a sense of community could enable a very human future within any of these scenarios.

- *What challenges might we face in adapting to each scenario?*
- *What are the most pressing implications for government, business, the energy sector, and education in these different futures?*
- *What might be the critical steps to enable our preferred scenario?*

A version of this chapter was originally published in Software Testing News under the title "Scenarios for the Future of Energy."

20 Ways Business Meetings and Events Might Change in the Next Five Years

Rohit Talwar, Steve Wells, Alexandra Whittington, Helena Calle, and
April Koury

How might the events sector change to meet the needs of an
increasingly digitized delegate community?

Forces Shaping the Future of Meetings

The next five years promise to bring fundamental changes across society—from the clients we serve, to the technology we use, and the needs and priorities of business—literally everything is up for grabs. At the same time, societal shifts, changing delegate and employee expectations, economic turbulence, and financial uncertainty will all add to this mix. Collectively, they will create complexity, new opportunities, unexpected challenges, and a pressure to stay ahead of the game in spotting what's next. Here we outline 20 developments that could potentially become major industry trends over the next five years. We start with two macro factors that could have global impact.

Macro Factor 1–New Inspiration

Conferences will have an increasingly interdisciplinary focus—in many sectors, participants will tire of hearing the same industry speakers and vendors saying roughly what they said last year! In the search for inspiration to maintain attendance levels, organizers will increasingly invite inspiring people from different fields—arts, science, music, business, education, or engineering—to share their ideas with participants. The convergence of people coming from different fields and those from the sector, will contribute to more creative ideas and solutions for the complex issues shaping the future of every sector.

Macro Factor 2–Global Economic Tensions

Businesses the world over are struggling to understand what form the UK's exit from the European Union might actually take—or if it will happen at all. Should it happen, the process might take five or ten years to complete fully. There is likely to be a high level of uncertainty and chaos. At the same time, we have growing concerns over the rise of economic nationalism and the possibility of trade wars between the USA and its major commercial partners. As these stories continue to unfold there will be growing demand for events which help suppliers to major economies understand the latest picture and implications for their sector. For the meetings industry, the key here will be the ability to organize and promote relatively short, high quality, sector-specific events at speed.

20 Meetings Industry Changes on the Horizon

1. *#metoo Charters*–The meetings industry will take positive action in the wake of the harassment and assault cases made public across many sectors in 2017 and 2018. Codes of conduct will appear covering behavior at events; participants will be asked to sign these to confirm their adherence. Reporting of incidents will be made easier and more discreet, and offenders' organizations will be notified immediately when such issues arise.
2. *Political Uncertainty*–For the travelers to the USA, uncertainty will continue over whether travel bans, or enhanced border vetting, will be in place for visitors from a range of countries. This may lead some organizers to locate global events in locations with no such restrictions.

3. ***Smarter by Design***–The deployment of artificial intelligence (AI) in the sector will expand rapidly. We are likely to see AI tools become a feature across the entire industry value chain. Applications will range from designing agendas, setting prices, and targeting potential attendees through to customer service chatbots, determining best fit locations, matchmaking people at events, and providing backup content and fact checking of presentations. In a very human business such as the events sector, it seems likely that AI will be used to free up time for value-adding tasks rather than reduce headcounts.

4. ***Business Model Experimentation***–In a world where new charging models are proliferating, there will be a growing pressure on events to bring greater creativity to bear. From paying based on the perceived value and seat auctions through to pay per session and results-based charging, the sector will be exploring a range of attendee payment ideas.

5. ***Silent Conferences***–Participants will be able to tune in to every parallel session via their personal devices and listen through their headphones from wherever they are in a venue. So, if the current session doesn't appeal, you can simply switch to listen to or watch another parallel session without leaving your seat.

6. ***Real-Time Conference Agendas***–Participants will be able to use meeting apps to schedule impromptu sessions held in any available space—coffee bars, lobbies, exhibition floors, even car parks. The speaker will talk into a microphone attached to their own smartphone and have the talk broadcast to those who tune in to that particular channel. Attendees will be able to view presentation slides and hear the speaker via their own device and headphones. So, no matter how noisy the background, the audience will be able to understand you perfectly clearly.

7. ***Next Generation Meeting Scheduling***–The intelligent assistants (IA) on our phone, or on the meeting app, will book appointments and meeting locations for us based on the types of people we say we want to meet. The IA will scan the attendee list, find the people

who fit the criteria we've defined, and then contact their IA to request and set up meetings.

8. *Stress Centers*—Concerns over our mental wellbeing are rising across society, and workplace stress is reaching epidemic levels in some sectors. Events will start to include facilities where participants can talk discretely to counselors and therapists about their issues.

9. *Thinking Hubs*—Meeting venues will have interactive technology that will enable creative thinking and idea testing. Interactive technologies such as virtual reality (VR) or augmented reality (AR) will allow participants to visualize data or ideas developed in a workshop session in a more tangible way. Participants will be able to test different ideas in VR/AR software and compare their possible outcomes to make better decisions.

10. *Integrated Events Apps*—Users will not have to download individual apps for each event. Integrated systems will emerge that present content for multiple events—these may even become standard features on many smartphones. App developers will create more cohesive systems that merge the information and presentations of all the different events that sign up to use them. Users will have the opportunity to browse for the most interesting and useful information across a range of events and conferences—perhaps making micro-payments to access content from the events they didn't attend.

11. *Digital Twins*—Early adopters of technology could soon be able to send a digital stand-in to attend face-to-face conferences. The participant's digital twin would be a software incarnation of the person embodied (or not) by a hologram or device that can see, hear, and observe the event in real time. The digital twin could engage with other participants in virtual space or on social media during the event, leading up to scheduled face-to-face meetings with interesting contacts at later points in time.

12. *Robot Realms*—Events will make greater use of robots as mobile customer service assistants, kitchen staff, baristas, waiting staff, security guards, and porters. We'll also see more robots featuring

in presentations and even delivering them. Within facilities we might see drones capturing videos of the sessions, transporting goods, and even moving people between sessions.

13. *Paradise Unplugged*–Some meetings will be elevated to a luxury experience by adopting technology-free policies that demand unplugging, disconnecting, powering down, and "off-gridding" for all participants. Events will set a tone of intimacy and authenticity by discarding the free Wi-Fi and discouraging conference hashtags, for example. The venues would provide a facility at check-in where participants can drop off their devices for the day and unplug, putting a total focus on the experience at hand.

14. *Cryptoculture*–With the rising profile of digital currencies like Bitcoin, the next five years could require the meetings sector to adapt to customers interested in paying with cryptocurrencies. Being prepared to accept payments via Bitcoin and other digital currencies would be an important step; there may also be new risks at hand when it comes to having anonymously paid fees, which is the nature of Bitcoin but unconventional in terms of event planning.

15. *Cryptoeventing*–There is likely to be a massive expansion of events about and related to blockchain and cryptocurrencies as investment interests grow and the public becomes more and more curious about the potential of both. A growing number of industry conferences will also look to add content about the potential impact and use of blockchain and cryptocurrencies in their sector.

16. *Circular Economies and Zero Waste*–The meetings and conference industry will come under growing pressure and take greater action to alleviate food, energy, and water waste. Scientific studies have shown that the Earth's ecosystems are weakening due to inefficiencies in current economic structures and distribution systems. So, for example, millions go hungry while fresh food is routinely discarded. Events and meetings that put into practice the principles of circular economies and zero waste, and philosophies that encourage reuse and discourage overconsumption, might

have a powerful role to play in the future where natural resources, even food, could be in short supply.

17. *The Replaced*–As the automation of work and jobs progresses as an economic force, it is possible that there will be a rise in the number of unemployed people due to technological disruption. Events and meetings aimed at this audience might emerge as an opportunity for the meetings sector. Past employers, governments, other sponsors, and even the individuals themselves might pay for seminars, conferences, education sessions, and certification courses aimed at counseling, reskilling, and retraining these displaced individuals. Indeed, these could become regular events in many local communities.

18. *Big Brother*–Events that gather large numbers of participants could become attractive to proponents of the growing Internet of Things (IoT) and smart city movement. Attendees of large events might earn rewards, discounts, or actual money for agreeing to use devices that track their movement and behavior during business conventions or meetings. Such attendee data would provide key insights to exhibitors, and non-participating marketers, for example those targeting the business traveler.

19. *Tracking Delegates*–Marketers will place ever-greater value on knowing how participants spend their time, which stands they visit, what they look at on specific exhibits, who they talk to, and how long for. Of course, this might all seem very intrusive, so it would need to be the choice of the individual attendee as to whether they were tracked or not. For event venues, large exhibition spaces might provide the perfect venue for IoT vendors to set up demonstrations and smart city simulations.

20. *Enhanced-Friendly*–People are beginning to pursue a range of brain and body enhancements—chemical, genetic, physical, and electronic. From nootropic attention-stimulating drugs and supplements through to body strengthening exoskeletons, and genetic modification, the sci-fi notion of "bodyhacking" is becoming a reality. Event planners will increasingly need to consider the needs of these enhanced visitors. As biohacking and

bionics go from fringe to mainstream, how will meeting planners adapt to dealing with customers, colleagues, and vendors who are partially enhanced? Within the next five years, various forms of biotech implants could become more normalized, giving some individuals superhuman hearing, vision, or memory. As the sensory spectrum is expanded, will meetings be expected to accommodate the needs of the enhanced human?

The Point of No Return

The next five years could see more dramatic change taking place in the meetings sector than we have seen since its emergence. A powerful combination of economic, social, technological, and environmental factors will create new opportunities and challenges and force the sector to undertake a fundamental rethink of literally every aspect of what it does. Some will act fast to be ahead of the curve and use these impending changes as an opportunity to innovate in advance of the competition; others will inevitably wait until they are forced to by customers and competitive pressures. The choice over when to act is down to the individuals involved—but panic and crisis driven strategies rarely provide sustainable business advantage.

- *Other than technology, which areas of the economy, life, and society might have the biggest future impact on the events and meetings industry?*
- *How might the job roles in your organization be impacted by some of the 20 trends described above?*
- *What might be some of the critical skills required to ensure a viable future for businesses in the meetings and conference sector?*

A version of this chapter was originally published in Entrepreneur and Investor under the title "Entrepreneurial Opportunities as the Business Meetings & Events Sector Changes in the Next Five Years."

Artificial Intelligence and the IT Professional

Rohit Talwar, Steve Wells, Alexandra Whittington, and Maria Romero

How might the IT profession be reshaped by intelligent machines?

A Catalyst for Change

Technology workers are on the front lines of a major breakthrough in work productivity and business performance: artificial intelligence (AI). The central role of AI in the future of almost every sector is practically a given. Business and technology analysts the world over agree that AI will have an impact across all industries. For the IT profession, the future could involve being called upon to work with AI, develop AI solutions, and potentially help their customers strike the perfect balance in work design between technology and people.

Almost every new technology arrives with a fanbase claiming it will revolutionize life on Earth. For some, AI is just one more in a long list of over-hyped technologies that won't live up to its promise. At the other end of the spectrum are those who believe this could literally be the game-changing innovation that reshapes our world. They argue that humanity has a directional choice: Do we want the transformation to enable an unleashing of human potential, or lead us toward the effective end of life on the planet? We believe AI is like no technology that has gone before, but we also think we are far too early in its evolution to know how far and how rapidly this Fourth Industrial Revolution powered by smart machines might spread. So, what broader issues do IT professionals need to be mindful of to ensure that we go beyond genuine stupidity in preparing for artificial intelligence?

Unquantifiable Economic Impact?

There are numerous attempts being made to predict the overall impact of AI on employment at a national and global level, and where the skill shortages and surpluses might be in the coming decades. In practice, the employment outlook will be shaped by the combination of the Fourth Industrial Revolution, the decisions of powerful corporations and investors, the requirements of current and "yet to be born" future industries and businesses, an unpredictable number of economic cycles, and the policies of national governments and supra-national institutions.

Collectively, the diverse economic factors at play here mean it is simply too complex a challenge to predict with any certainty what the likely progress of job creation and displacement might be across the planet over the next two decades. Globally, many of the analysts, forecasters, economists, developers, scientists, and technology providers involved in the jobs debate are also largely missing or avoiding a key point here. In their contributions, they either don't understand, or are deliberately failing to emphasize, the self-evolving and accelerated learning capability of AI and its potentially dramatic impact on society. If we do get to true artificial general intelligence or artificial superintelligence, then it is hard to see what jobs might be left for the humans. Hence, through the pages of our recent book, *Beyond Genuine Stupidity—Ensuring AI Serves Humanity*, we argue that perhaps a more intelligent approach is to start preparing for a range of possible scenarios.

Emergence of New Societal Structures?

The potential scale and spread of the impacts of AI raise issues for IT professionals that simply haven't been a major consideration with previous technologies. For example, right now, many in society are blissfully unaware of how AI could alter key social structures. For example, if the legal system could be administered and enforced by AI, would this mean that we have reached the ideals of fair access, objectivity, and impartiality? Or, on the contrary, would the inherent and unintended bias of its creators define the new order? If no one has to work for a living, would children still need to go to school? How would people spend their newfound permanent free time? Without traditional notions of employment, how will people pay for housing, goods, and services?

For wider society, what might the impacts of large-scale redundancies across all professions mean for the prevalence of mental health issues? Would societies become more human or more techno-centric as a result of the pervasiveness of AI? How would we deal with privacy and security concerns? What are the implications for notions such as family, community, and the rule of law? These are just a few of the key topics where the application of AI could have direct and unintended consequences that challenge our current assumptions and working models and will therefore need to be addressed in the not so distant future. An inclusive, experimental, and proactive response to these challenges would help ensure that we are not blindsided by the impacts of change and that no segment of society gets left behind. These issues give a sense about how the focus and nature of IT roles could evolve over the next decade.

New Challenges for Business and Government?

With many technologies in recent history, businesses have had the luxury of knowing that they can wait until they were ready to pursue their adoption. For most firms, they could be relatively safe in the assumption that being late to market wouldn't necessarily mean their demise, so they are treating AI the same way. Furthermore, a predominantly short-term, results driven focus and culture has led to many ignoring or trivializing AI because it is "too soon to know," or worse, suggesting "it will never happen." Finally, those at the top of larger firms are rarely that excited by any technology and can struggle to appreciate the truly disruptive potential of AI.

However, the exponential speed of AI developments means that the pause for thought may have to be a lot shorter. There's a core issue of digital literacy here, and the more data-centric our businesses become, the greater the imperative to start by investing time to understand and analyze the technology. From the top down, we need to appreciate how AI compares to and differs from previous disruptive advancements and grasp its capability to enable new and previously unimaginable ideas and business models. Already three domains of application are emerging—firstly, processing data on a scale that is beyond human capability—for example, scanning thousands of people's faces in seconds to identify potential security risks in a busy shopping mall. Secondly, automating entire tasks such as processing an insurance claim, and finally, augmenting human decision support in areas like medical diagnosis by identifying the statistically most likely causes of a patient's symptoms. Within our businesses, we need to understand the potential for AI to unlock value from the vast arrays of data we are amassing by the second. We also need to become far more conscious of the longer-term societal impact and the broader role of business in society.

Call it corporate social responsibility or enlightened self-interest, but either way, businesses will have to think much more strategically about the broader societal ramifications of operational decisions. Where will the money come from for people to buy our goods and services if firms in every sector are reducing their headcounts in favor of automation? What is our responsibility to the people we lay off? How should we respond to the notion of robot taxes? How could we assure the right balance between humans and machines, so the technology serves people?

Clearly there is some desire in business today to augment human capability and free up the time of our best talent through the application of AI. However, the evidence suggests that the vast majority of AI projects are backed by a business case predicated on reducing operational costs—largely in the form of humans. Some are already raising concerns that such a narrowly focused pursuit of cost efficiency through automation may limit our capacity to respond to problems and changing customer needs. Humans are still our best option when it comes to adapting to new developments, learning about emerging industries, pursuing new opportunities, and innovating to stay abreast or ahead of the competition in a fast-changing world. Business leaders must weigh up the benefits of near-term cost savings and taking humanity out of the business, against the risk of automating to the point of commoditizing our offerings.

Governments are clearly seeing the potential—and some of the risks and consequences—of AI. For example, the Chinese government is estimated to be investing US$429 billion across national, regional, and local government to ensure it becomes a global leader in AI. The Finnish government has provided an online platform for all its citizens to learn about AI for free. The UK government has announced plans to invest over US$1 billion in AI, broadband, and 5G technology, and a further US$530 million to support the introduction of electric autonomous vehicles.

However, governments are also confronted by tough choices on how to deal with the myriad issues that are already starting to arise: Who should own the technology and direct its likely power? What measures will be needed to deal with the potential rise of unemployment? Should we be running pilot projects for guaranteed basic incomes and services? Should we be considering robot taxes? What changes will be required to the academic curriculum? What support is required by adult learners to retrain for new roles? How can we increase the accessibility and provision of training, knowledge, and economic support for new ventures?

How IT Professionals Can Ensure AI Serves Humanity

The ability of smart machines to undermine human workers is a valid threat, but it doesn't have to be a death sentence, especially if the tech worker of tomorrow is enlightened about AI. One of the best ways to guarantee that AI will serve humanity is to keep it beneficial but benign: exploit the benefits but reject the aspects which threaten the greater good. If the choice is made to ensure that AI does not unravel the basic support systems for society, future IT staff might find themselves in a social profession providing a public service. By 2030, could the exercise of technological expertise come across as an act of humanity, rather than a commercial transaction? Such drastic transformation would be a startling development, yet somehow resonates with previous technological breakthroughs, like the internet, which led to entirely new economic systems, business models, and jobs—most notably creating the entire IT profession. In what ways will AI have similar ramifications? Information and ideas about the potential futures of AI are an antibody giving businesses a jolt of immunity against genuine stupidity about technological disruption.

- *Does the IT worker of the future have an obligation to defend humanity?*
- *Which forms of AI seem to pose the biggest existential threat?*
- *How will the IT industry of the future use AI?*

A version of this chapter was originally published in IT Pro Portal under the title "Just Another Disruptive Technology? The Future of Artificial Intelligence."

AI in Financial Services— Applications and Challenges

Rohit Talwar

Are you prepared for artificial intelligence to take greater control of financial services?

Financial Services Embraces AI

Clear away the vendor hype and desperate "me too" announcements from across the sector, and the evidence is starting to mount that financial services is exploring serious applications of artificial intelligence (AI). The technology is being deployed in everything from complex internal reconciliations, risk identification, and fraud detection through to customer service chatbots, robo-trading, and targeted marketing based on deep customer profiling. Furthermore, in the fast-paced world of FinTech start-ups, we are seeing AI-powered hedge funds and advisory firms, personal finance managers, and a host of sites that offer us the potential to streamline traditionally slow and expensive processes for everything from invoice financing to personal insurance.

Evolutionary Applications

So, now the game is on, where can we see things evolving to in the coming years? One area is in real-time fraud detection for banking and credit card transactions—spotting and preventing situations that might otherwise take us weeks to resolve. At another level, investors and regulators could eventually be able to monitor the behavior of fund managers and personal advisors. These systems would examine transactional behavior, personal spending patterns, and social media activity to detect the potential for insider trading, market manipulation, and misuse of client funds.

For individuals, the aggregation of our personal data with that of millions of other people will allow our intelligent finance advisors to recommend cheaper alternatives for goods and services we buy regularly. The next step would be to aggregate our purchasing to secure discounts from key suppliers. Indeed, we might authorize these advanced comparison tools to switch our purchases, insurances, and even savings on a continuous basis to whoever is offering us the best deal.

New Opportunities

Taking this a stage further, new opportunities might arise for those who have a detailed understanding of our lifestyles from travel, to dining, and clothing purchases and can link this to our personal financial management. Such sites might be authorized to trade unused airmiles and store loyalty points on our behalf, negotiate entertainment discounts for us, accept paid adverts to our social networks, and rent out our driveway as a parking space. Such systems would then invest any cash surpluses earned on a moment by moment basis using our preferred risk profile as a guide.

The next evolution might be to employ a personal AI clone or "digital twin." These applications would build a detailed understanding of our lifestyles and be authorized to buy, save, sell, or trade on our behalf. Depending on the level of authorization, they might undertake credit card purchases, bank transactions, and bill payments, complete loan or mortgage applications, and even make impulse buys. The system might report back on every transaction or simply deliver an end of day voice or video mail to update on the day's activities.

Limitless Applications

The list of potential applications is literally limitless. From streamlining and reducing the cost of activities that are currently an expensive hassle, through to finding new ways of making our finances go further, AI seems increasingly likely to become a vital part of the financial ecosystem. While many of the new AI ventures will go the way of most start-ups and fade away, some will survive. Furthermore, the best ideas are likely to be adopted by more established players as they seek to transform themselves into more customer-centric enterprises. The hope is that successive waves of AI innovation will help us make far better use of all the assets at our disposal—not just our cash—and deliver far more efficient, personalized, and personable financial services.

- *What new services would appeal to you?*
- *What reassurances do you need that AI will use your identity in the way you want?*
- *How much of your financial life would you be prepared to hand to your digital assistant?*

A version of this chapter was originally published in Finovate under the title "Beyond the Hype: AI in Financial Services Gets Serious."

A Perfect Storm? Factors Driving the Risks of Financial Armageddon

Rohit Talwar, Steve Wells, Alexandra Whittington, Helena Calle, and
April Koury

What are the potentially disruptive forces that could drive the next
global financial crisis?

Thinking the Unthinkable

Financial meltdowns are generally not caused by completely unexpected shocks. Typically, warning signals are visible to those close to the action who know where the fragilities are. The problem is that we may not know how to act pre-emptively, or don't want to move first for fear of disproportionately adverse outcomes for our business, sector, or nation. Often, we simply don't want to think about potential problems and disasters as we are not so well equipped to navigate through them. So, there can be a tendency to ignore or wave away warning signals and those who raise them. As futurists, our role is to help leaders address these issues by exploring the factors shaping the future, thinking the unthinkable about potential shocks, and examining how these might all combine into different scenarios.

Here, we deliberately focus on potential shock factors that could combine and accelerate, leading to a financial Armageddon scenario.

We go on to explore actions financial advisors can take to help prepare and protect their clients.

New Systemic Risks

The 2007-08 meltdown led to a raft of new legislation and controls. However, while some high-risk products and questionable practices may have been stamped out, there are concerns that a range of even more devastating financial timebombs lie ticking under the surface. These start with relatively well-known concerns like unserviceable personal, corporate, and national debt, heavily debt-exposed banks, and pension fund deficits.

The challenges extend to newer and more exotic flavors of risk emerging from artificial intelligence (AI) and blockchain-based products and services that are difficult to comprehend and regulate. These include highly complex algorithmically generated and traded assets and volatile, bubble-like markets for cryptocurrencies, initial coin offerings (ICOs), tokenized asset offerings, and entirely digital decentralized autonomous organization (DAO) trading entities that currently seem to lie beyond the comprehension and control of many financial regulators.

The Rush to FinTech

An economic downturn could see accelerated movement of funds into the new asset classes and digital product and service platforms emerging across financial sectors. The FinTech boom is accelerating and expanding its focus from platforms to new asset classes as outlined above, attracting billions of dollars from traditional investors and newcomers. The mainstream financial services sector has been left somewhat flat footed by FinTech and is seeing competitors offering traditional services at a fraction of the cost. The spectrum of offerings gaining traction include algorithmic hedge funds (e.g. Numerai), crowdfunded corporate debt (WiseAlpha), peer-to-peer lending (Lending Crowd, Zopa), digital banks (Monzo, N26), financial advice (Pefin), robo-trading (Collective2), and copy trading (Covesting).

Trade Wars, Sanctions, and a Global Stock Market Meltdown

A significant expansion of the trade conflict between the USA and China could lead to dramatic revenue reduction, stock market collapses, and job losses in both economies and spread globally. This could be exacerbated through wider sanctions against Russia, Iran, Qatar, and other nations challenging the "world order."

Escalation of Armed Conflict and Instability

International and intranational conflicts appear to be on the rise. Several potential flashpoints could disrupt energy and raw material supplies and spook global markets. Key here are tensions between the UK, USA, and NATO and Russia; Saudi Arabia and Iran; and Gulf coalition countries and Qatar. While armed engagement in the South China Seas seems lower on the risk register, there is still significant potential for flashpoints between the USA and China that could set the world on edge.

Brexit Downturn

While peace may break out between Britain and the EU over the terms of the exit, the medium- to long-term outcomes remain uncertain. A poorly managed Brexit could be calamitous, triggering a prolonged global recession. Through the exit and transition period, the UK could become mired in the change process. Most government departments will have to focus on extraction from the European Union (EU) and put in place mechanisms to replace those of the EU. The costs of withdrawal, implementing new systems such as customs, and recruiting staff into government could result in cuts in spending in several areas such as welfare payments and infrastructure development.

Foreign companies may accelerate withdrawal of key operations from the UK and automation may accelerate as firms reduce risks by cutting staff costs—swapping machines for humans. Markets may be further unsettled by transition uncertainties and an extended rebalancing period for the economy. The outcome could see massive public and private sector job cuts, rising import costs, significant declines in government tax revenues, consumers switching from spending to saving, and higher levels of personal debt. Uncertainty could also drive more company failures, declining corporate investment, a growing number of empty commercial buildings and retail outlets, falling domestic and commercial property prices, rising poverty levels, and higher social welfare costs. In response, share indices could fall 20% or more, with GDP collapsing by 6-10%, the pound reaching dollar parity, and unemployment hitting 20%. The UK economy could nosedive into a multi-year recession.

Global Economic Slowdown

Since the financial crisis, many economies have stabilized, enjoying increasing GDP, rising employment, and stock market growth. However, the factors above could trigger abrupt global retrenchment. Furthermore, contagion effects from the Brexit scenario could engulf the planet, fueling further chaos. Additional contributory factors could include rising nationalism, and more widespread tariff barriers. Domestic debt problems, declining consumption, and tougher export markets could also hamper global growth engines like China, India, Indonesia, Germany, Mexico, the Philippines, and Malaysia.

Technology Sector Collapse

A technology backlash could lead or amplify global market reverses and economic decline. Apple, Alphabet (Google), Amazon, Microsoft, and Facebook are the five most valuable public companies on the planet by market capitalization. The uplift in global stock indices in recent years, can in part be attributed to growing dominance of these players in consumer and business markets. Furthermore, most growth predictions for the future place a significant emphasis on technology sector expansion and exponential growth of new entrants, sectors, products, and services. Some believe the pushback is already happening. For example, President Trump's hostility toward Amazon is adding to rising public anger fueled by Facebook's privacy issues, the growth of surveillance capitalism, and mounting concerns over the potential adverse economic impacts of AI.

AI and Cliff Edge Automation

Exponential automation technologies such as AI, robotics, blockchain, cryptocurrencies, autonomous vehicles, and 3D/4D printing could drive rapid replacement of humans—a process that has already started in several sectors such as retail, logistics, and financial services. This might catalyze a near-term collapse in consumer spending and tax revenues, while driving up unemployment benefit and welfare claims. For the medium to longer term, it is almost impossible to make meaningful predictions of the impacts, because it is unclear whether we will see displaced jobs replaced in full by new opportunities. The hope is that jobs will emerge in renewable energy, green and autonomous transport, synthetic biology, distributed micro-manufacturing, human augmentation, and new service sectors. However, they may be several years off and will require considerable workforce retraining.

The near-term concern is that physical robots and smart software could replace vast quantities of jobs in sectors like manufacturing, warehousing and logistics, transport, retail, construction, customer service, finance, and administration. Typically, these technologies are deployed in "cliff edge" implementations where 50% or more of the workforce could be rendered unnecessary overnight through automation.

Collapse of Major Businesses Across Sectors

A cluster of major businesses failing could lead to a domino effect that pulls others under and wreaks havoc in the economy and public markets. Recent failures of firms like Carillion, Maplin, and ToysRUs, have reinforced concerns that no business is immune from change or too big to fail. A rash of store closures by retailers such as Marks and Spencer and New Look in the UK also highlight the growing struggle firms face to compete in the new economy. Internet competition, new business models, high overheads, growing debt obligations, closed mindsets, and outdated assumptions could drive many to the brink. Nervous lenders and investors could pull the plug on "at risk" firms. This could drag down those further from the edge as their financiers become more risk-averse in their outlook.

Occupy V2.0–Social Upheaval

Collectively the factors outlined above might drive social unrest. This might take the form of boycotts of brands perceived to be automating in an insensitive manner, occupation protests, crippling cyber strikes, and physical attacks. Prime targets might include financial institutions and others considered to be profiting massively while others are driven to the breadline. A second wave of disruption might come from professions who feel public budget cutbacks have rendered their services untenable. Unrest is clearly starting to rise among groups as diverse as doctors, nurses, teachers, the military, police, and fire services.

A third and perhaps surprising shock might be a growing and progressively more disruptive challenge from women in the workforce to be treated as equal in every regard, immediately. There is growing frustration—from #metoo and #timesup—to appalling gender pay disparities revealed in company disclosures. The World Economic Forum estimates it will take 217 years to reach gender equality on pay and opportunities at current rates of progress. Indeed, that figure has worsened by 47 years in just one year. Concerted disruptive action by women across society could impact every sector, with serious economic consequences.

Five Key Actions

For advisors, such uncertainties pose immense challenges. As futurists, we suggest five key actions:

1. Track a wide range of risk factors and provide regular client updates and commentaries on developments and possible directions of travel. Hosting regular physical networking events would allow you to stay close to clients, hear their views on emerging issues, learn about their investment strategies and what opportunities they are seeing, and create collaboration opportunities between clients—all of which help raise your value to them.
2. Become historians and do the analysis to see which asset classes, sectors, and geographic markets have fared best in past crises.

3. Investigate emerging FinTech platforms and asset classes to understand how they work, risk factors, potential returns, and influencing forces.

4. Test and adopt smart online tools to scan the marketplace continuously—providing clients with information on everything from bond rates to new ICO and IPO announcements.

5. Investigate creating your own pooled investment fund using a publicly available platform. This would allow clients to invest in each other's businesses and participate in their third-party investments.

Positioning for Persistent Volatility

Immense volatility is likely to be the overriding backdrop for the UK and global economies for the decade ahead and beyond. The next two to three years could perhaps be the most uncertain with the interplay of factors such as trade tensions, a tech backlash, Brexit, the spread of AI, and automation. Developing an anticipatory radar, proactive options, and new approaches to adding value are likely to help ensure the best advisors survive and thrive the risks of financial Armageddon.

- *What do you see as the most potentially impactful and uncertain shocks and what scenarios might play out?*
- *How resilient is your strategy to the emergence of potentially disruptive factors?*
- *Which are the shock factors you and your organization are aware of and have preparedness for?*

A version of this chapter was originally published in Financial Times Adviser under the title "Ten Things that Could Cause Financial Armageddon."

PART 7: Conclusion

Mapping A Very Human Future

Rohit Talwar

How can we respond to technological shifts and create a genuine agenda for change that advances the prospects for all humanity?

Enriching Humanity in a Digitized World

We hope that this book has provided a broad, stimulating, and provocative exploration of the ideas, developments, issues, and potential solution paths to *A Very Human Future*. So, what are the next steps to go from insight and ideas to experimentation and impactful change? Below we outline a brief manifesto of 12 critical action areas that we must focus on as individuals, society, businesses, and governments if we are to avoid the risk of being overwhelmed by the scale of change on the horizon.

1. *Extraordinary Leadership*—In order for us to explore any and all of the ideas presented in this book, we need to develop leaders with a vastly expanded set of capabilities. What's good for business in the future will be ever-more intricately entwined with what's good for individuals, society, and nations. Our choices and their consequences will come under an exponentially more intense spotlight, and actions with negative outcomes could bring down businesses and governments at an increasing rate. Hence, the imperative must be to increase the investment in developing leaders who can understand and navigate a rapidly changing reality.

Key here will be taking leaders out into the world to engage with those who are developing and implementing the ideas, processes, and technologies that are reshaping our world.

2. *Digital Literacy*—Individuals, businesses, and governments alike need to acknowledge the central role of digital in all our futures, especially its relevance to our job prospects and to the health of economies and businesses. This means making the investment of time and money to learn about the technologies coming through, understand what makes them different from what already exists, and appreciate the scale of their potential impact. Governments can follow the example of Finland in providing a free online intro-duction, businesses should be prioritizing and ensuring high levels of digital awareness, and individuals need to take advantage of the wealth of free content available on the internet. There are literally no excuses for maintaining a lack of digital literacy.

3. *Education Systems*—Across the globe, education systems, corporate learning programs, and adult education provision need upgrading. We need to ensure that these prepare people with the skills and awareness that will help them move easily from job to job and to create their own businesses. Proven accelerated learning models about that can help individuals acquire new knowledge and content rapidly. These approaches need to be accompanied with the acquisition of lifelong skills such as problem solving, collaboration, scenario thinking, and conflict resolution.

4. *Evaluating the Exponentials*—With governments and businesses, in particular, there is a tendency to be too slow and conservative in the evaluation of and experimentation with emerging technologies. The result can be crisis responses when the impacts become far greater and more wide ranging than expected. Initial evaluations therefore need to take an outside-in perspective, drawing on input from outside the organization and relevant discipline to gather a much broader set of views. The earlier we have a feel for possible development paths, application opportunities, and potential impacts, the more comprehensive and effective our response strategies should be.

5. *Employer Responsibilities*—In a world where technology may replace more jobs than it creates in the short term, we need a new debate about where the boundaries of employer responsibility lies. Be that helping staff with finding new jobs to paying higher taxes, the conversation and experimentation with different options needs to start yesterday. Equally, employers need to explore how they will navigate the boundaries between technologies that allow us to monitor every aspect of employee performance and behavior and the privacy, rights, and freedoms of the individual.

6. *Support for Job Creation*—Governments and businesses alike will have an interest in ensuring that new meaningful jobs are created for those rendered unemployed by automation. Whether as customers or taxpayers, there is a need in the current economic model for people to be earning money. Hence, an expansion and improvement in the quality of retraining schemes will be critical, as will a massive increase in support for those wanting to start their own businesses. Experimentation is required to test out a range of options.

7. *Investment in the Jobless*—A number of experiments are already underway with variants of guaranteed basic income schemes. Every nation will need its own exploration of policy options and to conduct experiments for how it will support potentially rising numbers of unemployed people, how it will help them retrain, and how it can address the broader societal consequences of declining employment.

8. *Creation of New Sectors*—From human augmentation to autonomous vehicles and synthetic materials, we will see a number of new industries emerge and hopefully generate jobs. Governments need to assess the likely loss of jobs in current sectors. The results need to be compared to the potential for job creation through current levels of investment in research and development, supporting new ventures, and attracting inward investment. Where there are clear gaps, action needs to be taken rapidly to avoid the potential for a rise in long-term unemployment. Many of the new jobs will require the equivalent of a degree level education. This in turn points to

the need to ensure anticipatory action in reshaping education curricula and supporting people to enter higher education.

9. *Addressing the Mental Health Issues*—Across the planet, stress has become a growing challenge, with rising numbers affected and a massive associated economic impact. Addressing this means changing workplace cultures and management models, increasing provision of mental health support in society, and expansion in the number of people being trained to become therapists and counselors in the future.

10. *Technology Ethics*—There is a challenge of trying to enforce global standards and guidelines on technologies that nations see as a core source of future competitive advantage. There is also the concern about the weaponization of technology and the protection of personal privacy. Nations and businesses alike have to take the lead in establishing clear codes of conduct on the technologies and their applications and demonstrate that they are holding themselves to the highest ethical standards. Citizen and consumer pressure will then act as a powerful lever on those who are slow to respond, although there will always be countries and companies that choose to sit outside such agreements.

11. *Draw Constructively on the Past*—Creating a very human future doesn't require that we erase the past. It is important to honor human history and retain the positive aspects. Ways of doing so might differ between cultures and countries, but the essence remains the same: uphold values and behaviors that place people at the center of all agendas. If we carry forward the elements of our past that celebrate humanity in all its forms, we can build a very human future at every level of technological development.

12. *A Very Human Dialogue*—The debate about whether particular advances harm or advance society's interests will rumble on, the key here is to maintain an open public dialogue. The challenge is to raise literacy levels and public awareness of the issues, so we can bring more citizens into the discussion to share their views on what society needs and wants as compared to what technology makes possible.

FAST FUTURE

Fast Future is a professional foresight firm specializing in delivering keynote speeches, executive education, research, and consulting on the emerging future and the impacts of change for global clients. In 2015 we created a new model of publishing led by three futurists— Rohit Talwar, Steve Wells, and April Koury. As a publisher, our goal is to profile the latest thinking of established and emerging futurists, foresight researchers, and future thinkers from around the world, and to make those ideas accessible to the widest possible audience in the shortest possible time.

Our *FutureScapes* book series is designed to address a range of critical agenda-setting futures topics with in-depth contributions from global thought leaders and cutting-edge future thinkers. We cover topics that we believe are relevant to individuals, governments, businesses, and civil society. Our *Fast Future* series is designed to provide rapid insights into the emerging future with a collection of short, hard-hitting articles. These explore different trends, developments, forces, and ideas shaping the future and how we can respond in a manner that best serves humanity.

Our first book, *The Future of Business*, provides 60 fast-moving chapters and 566 pages of cutting-edge thinking from 62 future thinkers in 21 different countries on four continents. Traditional publishers would take two years to deliver a book of this magnitude; we completed the journey from idea to publication in just 19 weeks. We have also created an innovative business model that bypasses most of the traditional publishing practices and inefficiencies, embracing digital era exponential thinking and applying it to transform the publishing process and the distribution approach. Our publishing model ensures that our authors, core team members, and partners on each book share in its success. Additionally, a proportion of profits are allocated to a development fund to finance causes related to the core topic.

We hope that our story and our approach to publishing are an inspiring example of how business is evolving and being reinvented in the digital era. Over the coming years, *Fast Future* aims to publish the work of insightful and inspiring futurists and future thinkers. We are keen to receive proposals from potential authors and those interested in compiling and editing a multi-contributor book as part of either the *FutureScapes* or *Fast Future* series.

For corporate or bulk orders of *A Very Human Future* or any of our books, please contact karolina@fastfuture.com.

To book a keynote speaker, discuss an executive education, consulting, or research requirement, or explore partnership opportunities, please contact rohit@fastfuture.com.

To submit a chapter idea or a book proposal, discuss ideas for curating and editing a multi-contributor project, or to enquire about permanent and internship opportunities, please contact info@fastfuture.com.

You can learn more about us at www.fastfuture.com. We look forward to hearing from you!

ALSO FROM FAST FUTURE

THE FUTURE OF BUSINESS
–Critical insights to a rapidly changing world from 62
future thinkers

The Future of Business is aimed at the leaders of today and the pioneers of tomorrow. Our intention is to provide a broad perspective on the key forces, trends, developments, and ideas that could redefine our world over the next two decades. The goal is to highlight how these future factors are shaping the opportunities, challenges, implications, and resulting choices for those driving the future of business. The book draws on the ideas of 62 futurists, future thinkers, and experts in a range of domains from 22 countries on four continents. *The Future of Business* highlights how—in a world of constant and ever-more fundamental change—those charged with leadership, management, and stewardship of large and small organizations alike are faced with a set of questions many of us never thought we would have to confront.

This book is designed to provide wide-ranging visions of future possibilities and take us on a tour of the forces shaping the political, economic, and social environment. We explore the advances in science and technology that could have the greatest impact on society and drive business disruption. We examine the implications of these for how business will need to evolve and the new industries that could emerge over the next two decades. We highlight key tools, approaches, and ways of thinking about the future that can help organizations embed foresight at the heart of the management model. We conclude with a framework that highlights key choices we face in shaping *The Future of Business*.

THE FAST FUTURE BOOK SERIES

This series of books is designed to provide clear and rapid insights into the trends, forces, developments, and ideas shaping the future and the possible scenarios that could arise. Each book contains a collection of short, hard-hitting articles that explore different aspects of the emerging future and how we can respond in a manner that best serves humanity. The books are deliberately intended to be a rapid read—providing the reader with key information needed to get up to speed on relevant future issues—explaining what they are, and their possible implications for individuals, society, business, and government. The first two titles in the series are *Beyond Genuine Stupidity – Ensuring AI Serves Humanity* and *The Future Reinvented – Reimagining Life, Society, and Business*.

BEYOND GENUINE STUPIDITY
–Ensuring AI Serves Humanity

The first book in the *Fast Future* series explores critical emerging issues arising from the rapid pace of development in artificial intelligence (AI). The authors argue for a forward-looking and conscious approach to the development and deployment of AI to ensure that it genuinely serves humanity's best interest. Through a series of articles, they present a compelling case to get beyond the genuine stupidity of narrow, short-term, and alarmist thinking and look at AI from a long-term holistic perspective. The reality is that AI will impact current sectors and jobs—and hopefully enable new ones.

A smart approach requires us to think about and experiment with strategies for adopting and absorbing the impacts of AI—encompassing education systems, reskilling the workforce, unemployment and guaranteed basic incomes, robot taxes, job creation, encouraging new ventures, research and development to enable tomorrow's industries, and dealing with the mental health impacts. The book explores the potential impacts on sectors ranging from healthcare and automotive, to legal and education. The implications for business itself are also examined from leadership and HR, to sales and business ethics.

THE FUTURE REINVENTED
–Reimagining Life, Society, and Business

The second book in the *Fast Future* series explores the future transformations that could arise from the disruptive technological, scientific, social, and economic developments shaping the decade ahead. The authors offer a range of unique visions of different aspects of a future in which the very tenets of reality are undergoing deep and vital transformations. Through a series of chapters organized into three sections (transformations in life, industries, and business), they present holistic future scenarios that encourage strategic thinking about what lies beyond the hype.

Using a long-term futurist perspective, *The Future Reinvented* offers glimpses of the future in different business sectors such as legal, automotive, and sales as well as in different areas of everyday life like retirement, education, and health. Audiences will appreciate the vivid imagery which brings to life a number of different "futures," including workplace scenarios where people work side by side with artificial intelligence or robotic colleagues, can obtain physical enhancements to become smarter, stronger, or more psychologically resilient, or reside in a post-jobs world. The book provides a solid foundation for scenario thinking and planning, identifying signals of change, and interpreting signposts that serve as early warning signs for emerging futures.

Visit www.fastfuture.com for more information.

Available in 2018-19 from Fast Future

Unleashing Human Potential—The Future of AI in Business

The pace of business investment in and adoption of artificial intelligence (AI) is accelerating and the level of interest and activity is rising across all sectors. The intention is to provide a diverse set of perspectives on where the technology is going, how it is being deployed in business today, and how the capabilities, applications, and impact of AI could evolve over the next 3-10 years. The book is designed to have the broadest possible scope and will be co-edited by Rohit Talwar and Steve Wells.

50:50—Scenarios for the Next 50 Years

This book explores scenarios for the next 50 years, with 50 perspectives on possible futures from 50 different future thinkers around the world. The book is designed to have the broadest possible scope and is edited by global futurists Rohit Talwar and Alexandra Whittington. The book explores potential future scenarios over the next 50 years across a range of topic areas.

500 Futures Shaping Our World

It is critical that organizations are able to make sense of the range of different factors shaping the emerging operating environment. This book will list, describe, and put into context 500 different future factors, trends, emerging possibilities, developments, and predictions.

500 Futures will be curated by global futurists Rohit Talwar, Steve Wells, and Alexandra Whittington.

Leading Exponential Futures—A Handbook for Navigating Uncertainty

With the ever-increasing pace and scale of change, it is becoming increasingly clear that leadership will be a critical enabler to navigating the transition to a truly digitized world. This book, curated by global futurists Rohit Talwar and Alexandra Whittington, will explore the role of a futurist and the use of foresight in helping organizations navigate an uncertain and complex journey to the future.

The Next Five Years—The Unfolding Future of Work

Every organization is wrestling with the challenge of adjusting or reworking the "now" to prepare for an uncertain future. We all need to develop scenarios, make forecasts, and put plans in place—but how many of them end up in a folder, electronic or otherwise, waiting for when the managers get around to it? The aim of *The Next Five Years* is to overcome the reluctance to engage with an uncertain longer-term horizon by offering the reader bite-sized, actionable insights that will help prepare their organization for the immediate future or, equally likely, the present that they haven't had time to catch up with. The book will be edited by global futurist Rohit Talwar and technology journalist and speaker Guy Clapperton.

Accountancy 3.0—The Future of Accounting Services

This book reveals, for the first time, the impact of the Fourth Industrial Revolution and consequential far-reaching changes across and outside of the profession. The issues we address here will excite, irritate, and enlarge the thinking of accountants in practice around the world. *Accountancy 3.0* will be edited by global futurist Rohit Talwar and accounting futurist Mark Lee.

The Many Futures of Education and Learning
The book is designed to have the broadest possible scope about the future of education and learning at every stage—from nursery to adult learning. It will be edited by global futurists Rohit Talwar, Steve Wells, Alexandra Whittington, and education specialist Helena Calle.

Pathways to Sustainable Abundance
Building on the notion of creating a very human future explored in this book, *Pathways to Sustainable Abundance* will explore how we can put humanity at the center of the story and harness advances in science and technology in service of the greater social good.

Under Consideration
The landscape for potential publication topics is evolving rapidly and we are excited at the prospects of working on multi-author books under the *FutureScapes* and *Fast Future* series banners or partnering with innovative organizations who share our passion for exploring the future. We are currently considering books on a range of future related themes.

We are always interested to hear from authors who want to bring their ideas, knowledge, and insights to market with Fast Future.

Visit www.fastfuture.com for more information.